Britain's Nature Reserves

BRITAIN'S
Nature Reserves

E. M. NICHOLSON

LONDON
Country Life Limited

First published in 1957
by Country Life Limited
2-10 Tavistock Street, London W.C.2
Printed in Great Britain by
Billing and Sons Limited
Guildford and London

© *E. M. Nicholson 1957*

With thankfulness to

CHARLES ROTHSCHILD (1877-1921)
ARTHUR GEORGE TANSLEY (1871-1955)

and all the pioneers whose devotion, leadership and vision
gave rise to the National Nature Reserves of Great Britain.

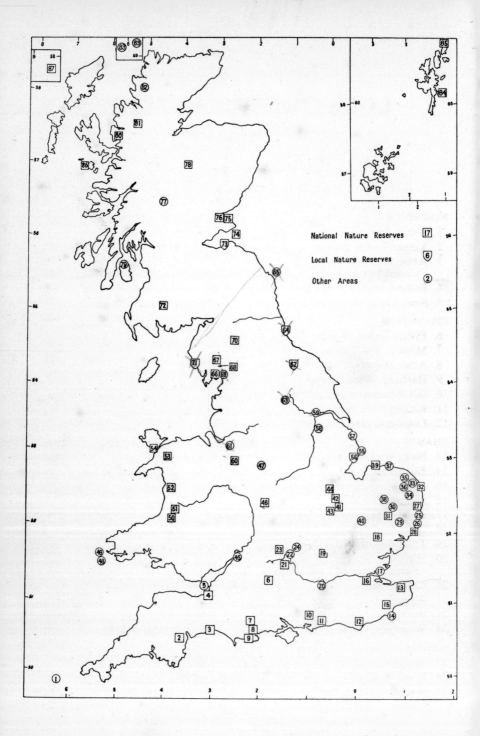

National Nature Reserves ▢17

Local Nature Reserves ⬡6

Other Areas ◯2

LOCATION OF NATURE RESERVES

The first number indicates the location of a Nature Reserve on the map opposite

ENGLAND AND WALES

SCOTLAND

CONTENTS

B

ILLUSTRATIONS

11

Plates 1, 11, 12, 17, 19, 34, 40, 44, 61 and 62 are reproduced by permission of the Air Ministry. Plates 2, 5, 6, 9, 10, 13, 14, 15, 18, 20, 22, 23, 25, 26, 27, 28, 32, 37, 39, 41 and 49 are reproduced by permission of the University of Cambridge. All of these photographs are Crown Copyright Reserved.

AUTHOR'S PREFACE

SOMEBODY had to write this book in order to explain the objects and scope of what may in a broad sense be called Nature Reserves, and especially of the part played in the general movement by the recently created Nature Conservancy. I have taken on the task because it is my good fortune to have seen most of them and to be in touch with their management and progress. I have tried to make the pictures and text of each Reserve help to illustrate the varied character and objects of the individual Reserves and the way they contribute to the larger scheme. In doing so I have had to draw upon much knowledge gathered by naturalists and others, past and present, and to traverse ground on which I must rely upon many experts in fields beyond my own competence. I am very much aware of my debt to them all and in particular to the officers of other organisations, landowners and scientists who have helped freely with advice and information.

I am also grateful to many of my colleagues within the Nature Conservancy for their valuable help and I must specially thank Miss Teresa Sexton, who has personally handled most of the raw material and has helped in innumerable ways with the production, and Mr B. H. Grimes, who has been largely responsible for meeting the exacting requirements for illustrations. While the Nature Conservancy have given me their approval and facilities for undertaking this work, responsibility for the opinions and statements in the book is entirely my own.

I would like to add two other points. Many countries have their Nature Reserves, and an Atlas of Nature Reserves in different countries has recently been produced with the help of the International Union for the Conservation of Nature and Natural Resources. My book, therefore, covers only a fragment of the Nature Reserves, even of Europe, and their numbers are so rapidly increasing both here and overseas that nothing published now can give more than a sample of those likely to exist in a few years' time.

Finally, may I remind all who may read this that disturbance is as great a menace to Nature as persecution, and that many Nature Reserves are best helped by being left in peace and quiet. Visiting Nature Reserves calls for restraint and discretion, and inconsiderate intrusion can only lead to a necessity for stricter limitations on access. This book is intended to help people to understand how to use Nature Reserves and when and where to leave them undisturbed. It is for all of us to prove that there is no truth in the saying that nature lovers to-day are in process of loving nature to death.

INTRODUCTION

NATURE is the oldest thing on earth, but Nature Reserves are among the youngest. In Great Britain Nature Reserves have only just passed through the pioneer and experimental stage. Even the idea of a Nature Reserve is still in process of emerging to its full definition and maturity in the world. The distinction between, for example, National Parks and Nature Reserves is still quite differently understood in different countries. In Switzerland they have a single National Park in which all visitors must keep strictly to a few paths and not stray off them, in order not to disturb wild life. Such a conception of a National Park would horrify English supporters of the movement, who would regard such an area as a very strict Nature Reserve, but they might well regard nearly all the rest of Switzerland as being what they would understand by an Alpine National Park, although the Swiss see it the opposite way round.

On the other hand, the Cairngorms Nature Reserve in Scotland is a large mountain area over which mountaineers and walkers are free to wander at will. It has almost all the features which, according to the British way of looking at things, constitute a National Park, but it is in fact a Nature Reserve, the mammals, birds and plants being largely protected by the climate and the extent and wildness of the ground.

Although the organised Nature Reserve is a fairly new thing, there was of course a time when for practical purposes the whole world was one great Nature Reserve without knowing it. As mankind multiplied and destroyed more and more natural habitats, the necessity for keeping some natural habitats inviolate began to be recognised. St Cuthbert started the first effective wild life refuge nearly thirteen hundred years ago on the Farne Islands, but the first big step in this direction was taken by the Norman Kings, who set aside the Royal Forests as what we would now call game reserves. The New Forest, for example, was created not for growing trees, but as a great open space in which the King could hunt, and very strict regulations were put on to protect the wild life. This conception of setting aside areas of wild country for sport has gone on in varying forms ever since, and it is still one of the principal reasons why some of the most valuable untouched natural areas have survived in this country.

It was only in the nineteenth century, with the great growth of human population and the increasing destructiveness of modern firearms, that the need began to be appreciated for areas to be protected against any kind of human interference. By the end of the century the Royal Society for the Protection of Birds, the National Trust and several local organisations were beginning to take steps to protect areas of special natural interest. Other societies followed, including the Society for the Promotion of Nature Reserves, which played probably the largest part in the movement after 1914. Its efforts, together with the Royal Society's complementary proposals for a Biological Service, resulted finally in the creation of the official Nature Conservancy under the auspices of the Privy Council in March, 1949.

In discussing Britain's Nature Reserves, we must therefore always bear in mind that they are of many different types. There are certain Nature Reserves which are examples of undisturbed habitats and are set aside entirely to preserve the fauna and flora, being as far as possible safeguarded against human intrusion or interference of any kind. There are others, especially where conditions are semi-natural or artificial, which are deliberately managed as Nature Reserves under some kind of intervention designed to maintain what is thought to be the most satisfactory situation. A number of these are open to the public and also serve recreational and other purposes, including in many cases grazing by sheep, cattle or horses. Then there are areas which are thought of and managed primarily as public open spaces but which are also very important refuges for interesting fauna and flora surviving in them despite the often rather intense disturbance. Also there are many areas such as the catchment areas of Water Boards, land owned by Defence Departments and by Hydro-Electric and other public authorities, and also by private persons, who manage them in a way which makes them for practical purposes Nature Reserves of a kind, although they are never officially so regarded. Some of these, however, are the subject of informal agreements or understandings for the protection of their wild life.

Then again, the Nature Reserves can be divided up into those which are managed by the Nature Conservancy on behalf of the Crown, those which are also managed under the 1949 National Parks and Access to the Countryside Act by County Councils, and those which are managed without statutory powers by other bodies, such as the Royal Society for the Protection of Birds, and local Trusts, such as the Norfolk and Lincolnshire Naturalists' Trusts. Again, there are the refuges set up for

1. Yarner Wood
Nature Reserve.
Distorted Oaks.

*2. Axmouth–Lyme Regis Nature Reserve.   Aerial view looking west along
Bindon Landslip showing on left the large area which in 1839 became separated
by the chasm at far end of which is the cliff from which Plates 3 and 4 were
taken.*

birds under the third clause, usually called the Sanctuaries Clause, of the Protection of Birds Act, 1954, and previous bird protection legislation.

There are certain differences which it is important to bear in mind between the British Nature Reserves and those of many other countries, particularly the United States, Canada and South Africa. First, the areas of Nature Reserves in this country are on the whole very small indeed compared with those in other continents. Our largest Nature Reserve in the Cairngorms is just under 40,000 acres, or about 62 square miles, and many of them are only a few hundred acres or even less than one hundred acres. By contrast the Kruger National Park in South Africa is a Nature Reserve covering 7,340 square miles or nearly a quarter of the area of all Scotland; while the Aleutian Islands National Wildlife Refuge of 4,250 square miles is roughly the size of Jamaica and larger than Cyprus.

A further important distinction is that almost the whole of Britain, however wild it may appear now, has been considerably modified by man or indirectly by his livestock, his fires, and his other interferences. It is, therefore, not possible to set aside large slices of nature in the raw, as it still is in other continents. The amount of management required to prevent development of quite unnatural conditions is much greater in Britain than in most other countries. Another somewhat unfortunate difference is that the lines between different types of land-use have become increasingly sharply drawn. In some other countries forests are managed not mainly or even largely for timber production, but equally for watershed control, wild life conservation, recreation and other purposes. Similarly, National Parks overseas are so set up that their degree of control over the land and their revenue resources enable them to play a large part in protecting wild life by means of rangers and wardens and in educating the public about it.

This is not possible in Britain where little nature conservation or education is undertaken by any bodies except those which exist solely for that purpose. As has already been mentioned, however, many bodies holding lands for other purposes do in fact provide refuges for wild life incidentally, and without giving it any special attention or putting any appreciable resources into it. On the other hand, in Britain as in the Netherlands it has been increasingly obvious to those responsible for Nature Reserves that their task can successfully be performed only if they take a very wide view of their responsibility, and above all if they acquire a deep scientific knowledge of the conditions governing

C

water levels, the evolution of vegetation and the balance of animal population. In Britain, therefore, Nature Reserves are regarded perhaps more than anywhere else as outdoor laboratories where the workings of nature can be studied, in addition to being outdoor living museums or wildernesses in which nature can be preserved as a national heritage.

We can, in fact, trace an evolution of ideas from the time when nature was regarded as quite capable of taking care of itself and as being in many ways stronger than civilisation, through the period when it was felt that no conservation was needed except of game for hunting and food and of big trees for the Navy, and from there to a conception of the rich but squandered natural inheritance of man and the need for conserving the most extensive possible range of examples of what the fauna and flora and landscape were like before they were roughly interfered with or destroyed. Most recently it has been appreciated that this task of preserving natural conditions is not simply one of putting a ring fence round certain wilderness areas and hoping for the best, but is dependent on knowledge and therefore on research. The emphasis has thus swung over to the scientific investigation (and where necessary management) of Nature Reserves, particularly in order to understand how to preserve interesting relics, conditions, habitats and species which would otherwise tend to disappear.

Nature protection was long regarded largely as a matter of passing the right laws, but it gradually came to be realised that it is one thing to pass a law and another to enforce it, and more recently it has been appreciated that a great part of nature protection cannot be covered by legislation at all, since it involves the protection of habitat which in turn involves land use and land management. Nevertheless, without the right framework of legislation nature protection in a modern, advanced civilisation is impossible.

In the matter of Nature Reserve legislation Great Britain is fortunately among the most advanced countries in the world. The principal statute is the National Parks and Access to the Countryside Act, 1949, which confers on the Nature Conservancy extensive powers to acquire Nature Reserves by statutory agreement or by the ordinary processes of purchase or lease (which are already provided in the Conservancy's Charter) and to declare these Nature Reserves, with the effect that they receive Crown Land status and that byelaws can be made prohibiting any actions on them which are contrary to the interests of wild life. Powers of compulsory acquisition were also conferred by this Act,

3. *Axmouth–Lyme Regis Slip, looking east, a photograph taken about 1905, showing scarcity of growth on bottom during first sixty-five years.*

4. *The Slip, looking east, a photograph taken in 1949.*

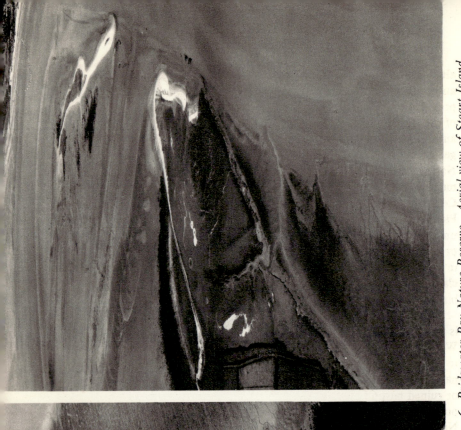

5. *Bridgwater Bay Nature Reserve. Aerial view to west.*   6. *Bridgwater Bay Nature Reserve. Aerial view of Steart Island.*

although the Conservancy have never sought to use them. Local authorities have the same powers to form Local Nature Reserves provided that they consult the Nature Conservancy over it. Section 23 of the Act requires the Nature Conservancy to notify to local planning authorities areas of special interest by reason of their flora, fauna or geological or physiographical features, and those which do not become Nature Reserves are given a certain degree of protection against development by the fact that the local planning authorities have to consult the Conservancy before consenting to their development in the sense of the Planning Act. A number of additional areas are made Bird Sanctuaries under Section 3 of the Protection of Birds Act, 1954, but this does not protect them against development, nor does it directly protect anything in them except the bird life. There is, however, a power under this clause to restrict access when it is detrimental to, for example, breeding birds.

Given such legislation, the first big task regarding Nature Reserves is to select the right places and to acquire them. Ever since the 1914-18 War local groups of naturalists have been carrying on surveys designed to show which are the most important surviving areas of outstanding national interest, and although many of these areas have been destroyed or ruined beyond effective use as Nature Reserves, a considerable proportion of them still remain and are the basis of the National series of Nature Reserves which is now coming into existence. The idea behind the selection is not to choose places on impulse or indiscriminately, but to build up a carefully balanced selection of the best surviving examples of different habitats ranging from coastal sand-dunes, shingle spits, salt marshes and sea cliffs to the grasslands of the limestone and chalk, the best examples of Oak, Ash, Beech, Pine and other woodlands natural to the country, and the waters, fens, bogs, heaths, moorlands and mountains. In this way it is hoped that on one or more of the National Nature Reserves it will be possible for scientists in the distant future to continue to have available for study first-class examples of each type of habitat which may at the present rate of loss have become completely extinct elsewhere. So far, over fifty National Nature Reserves have been acquired and declared, while about another twenty are in more or less advanced stages of negotiation. The total area is about 122,000 acres, of which nearly half are owned by the Nature Conservancy and the rest held under lease or Nature Reserve Agreement with the proprietors. Some of these National Nature Reserves are of all-round interest for their rocks, vegetation and animals of different kinds. Others are selected for some special feature, occasionally geological or physiographical, and in other cases to preserve some examples of special types of water, vegetation or fauna conditions, or in certain cases particular rare species or groups of species.

Having acquired these Nature Reserves the problems have hardly begun. The first task is to carry out a searching investigation not only of the plants and animals on the ground, but of the soil conditions, the development of erosion, the effects of past management policies, and everything else which has a bearing on the maintenance of the best conditions for wild life.

We may well be intimidated by the thought that even a moderate-sized woodland may sample about one-third of the entire British fauna. The trees, the flowering plants, the birds, the butterflies and moths and a few other groups are easy to see, but these are only a conspicuous minority of the species which form the woodland population. How can we even hope to discover what our wood contains and which of the obscure or minute species may really be playing some part, perhaps much more important than that of the species which immediately strike our eye?

Our starting point then must be to recognise with humility that whatever we do must be based more on ignorance than on knowledge, and that some at least of our interventions are likely to prove wrong. Nevertheless, experience with Nature Reserves shows that nothing can be more wrong than doing nothing when a habitat is rapidly deteriorating—for example, a grassland becoming overgrown with scrub, or a sheet of water becoming choked with vegetation, or a bird sanctuary becoming infested with crows and rats.

We begin then by trying to reduce our ignorance. Posterity can hardly condemn us for not recognising something which has not yet been discovered, but will blame us if we fail to find out everything possible about the problem which our Nature Reserve presents. First of all we must map it and survey it to the utmost possible extent. Geological large-scale maps, soil surveys and samples, vegetation surveys, plant lists, bird censuses, can be made without insuperable difficulty; and although they will not tell us everything, they will tell us a great deal directly and even more by inference. For instance, quite a number of species are indicators of some condition or historical feature. Wild Clematis or Old Man's Beard immediately tells us that there is plenty of lime in the soil; Sphagnum and Cotton Grass at the other extreme point to highly acid conditions; nettles show that the soil has been disturbed

fairly recently, almost always by human action. Elders, as an under-
storey in woodland, often indicate that it has been used as a roost,
usually by Starlings. In open places they, like Ragwort, are often
a pointer to a heavy rabbit population in the recent past, if not in the
present. Certain other plants and insects are pretty reliable evidence
that the soil has been under a woodland canopy for at least hundreds of
years.

Again, certain species of plants and animals are so frequently found
either together or not at all that they form what are known as communities or associations, which in turn can often be linked with particular
soil types or particular exposures or slopes, or some other factor in the
environment. Thus, a comprehensive and reliable list of the fauna and
flora of an area will tell an ecologist who has never been there a great
deal about the conditions of that area both now and even in the distant
past. Analysis of the pollen remains in peat or of the tree stumps preserved in it can tell us what the vegetation was many thousands of years
ago. Harvard University scientists have discovered how to trace in the
soil profiles under a woodland the spots where trees were blown down
up to hundreds of years ago, and so to trace the approximate dates of
the big storms which have affected that woodland.

Even plant and animal lists and comparatively superficial surveys
can, therefore, provide rich material for the first step in Reserve management, which is to ascertain what nature used to do with the area and
would do with it in the absence of human interference. In some cases,
as on shingle beaches or on the tops of high mountains, the answer may
be that what we see at the moment is exactly how nature would have it,
and management can therefore be confined to matters such as the control of collecting. In more fortunate continents the same often applies
to woodlands, fens and other habitats, but in Great Britain we almost
always find that man by over-grazing, over-burning, over-draining, cutting firewood or in all kinds of other ways has seriously modified the
habitat, leaving nature in a sick or partially crippled state. Sometimes
it is enough simply to bring to an end the interference and nature will
recover. Unfortunately, in many cases the end of interference will not
lead to a recovery of the primitive state, and it may not infrequently
lead to a worse situation than if the intervention were maintained. For
instance, grasslands which are properly grazed by sheep or cattle, or
fenlands where a moderate amount of peat cutting is done, or coppice
woodland where the coppice rotation is maintained, are preferable to
areas where similar treatment has been terminated with the result that

they become a prey to entirely unbalanced conditions bearing no resemblance to what they were like before human interference.

What is needed, therefore, is first an inventory or Domesday Book of everything that we can learn about the site, followed by the most skilful interpretation we can make of the past history and probable future trends, followed by a considered plan of management which will show whether any intervention is necessary and if so indicate the type of intervention proposed, the advantages and dangers anticipated from it, and if possible some small-scale experiments which will enable us to test the practical results of the proposed treatment before it is put into operation on a full-scale basis.

Even this, however, is not all, because in so far as Nature Reserves are open-air laboratories, scientists may want to work in them in ways which will involve interfering with some of the animals and plants. If the Nature Reserve is of irreplaceable value, no such researches can be permitted in it. It may be necessary even to refuse permission for any scientists to enter it if by so doing they might, for instance, lead some rare and shy breeding birds to desert. In other cases it is possible to set aside one zone in the Reserve in which reasonable scientific experiments can be made, but this requires the drawing up of a plan of scientific research in order to make sure that one research does not interfere with another. Many ecological researches have to continue for a series of years before they lead to any result and if, say halfway through that period, the environment is altered or interfered with, the work of several years may be made useless.

A decision, therefore, has to be made on what kinds of researches are to be carried on in which parts of the Reserve in order not to interfere with one another or with the welfare of the fauna and flora. Some of these researches may involve collecting animals and plants or marking animals with radio-active tags or clearing vegetation mechanically or by herbicides or making or diverting water courses.

Paradoxically we can ensure the survival of wild places of Britain only by finding out what happens when we interfere with them. It is, however, essential that all significant interferences should be very carefully considered and recorded, particularly where destruction or uncontrollable developments might be involved. In spite of their dangers, such researches when properly conducted are well worth while. Without them we would remain permanently in the dark about the techniques and results of Nature Reserve management and we would forfeit the dividend in advancement of knowledge and in the application of know-

7. *Steep Holm Island, Bristol Channel. Aerial view, showing landing beach at the east end and northern cliffs where the cormorant colony is located.*

8. *Steep Holm Island. Wild Peony, with a background of Privet.*

9. *Fyfield Down Nature Reserve. Aerial view showing Herepath and Sarsen Stones (crossing left to right)*

ledge to agriculture, forestry, water supply and other activities which they will yield.

At the same time Nature Reserves are a kind of estate and like other estates they need maintenance. Fences must be kept up, bridges repaired, paths and roads kept in reasonable condition, yet many of the tidying-up operations which would be normal on an ordinary estate are anathema on Nature Reserves, where, for instance, dead trees should be left lying where they fall. Nearly 600 species of small animals inhabit dying and dead deciduous wood in this country, and contrary to common belief it is not true that any appreciable proportion of them can be regarded as pests.

In addition, there are problems of public control. Are the public to have unlimited access, and if so is collecting to be restricted or permitted without restraint, which is rarely tolerable on a Nature Reserve? If not, how are permits to be issued and their conditions enforced? How are people to be discouraged from doing things in the Nature Reserve which would damage the wild life?

All sorts of other questions have to be taken into account in the management plan. How serious is the risk of fire and at what seasons is it greatest? What precautions can be taken to prevent outbreaks or to confine them to a small area? If outbreaks occur, how are they to be fought? Is it possible for anyone to break their necks, or drown themselves, or otherwise get into trouble on the Reserve, and what provisions should be made against such contingencies? Do people try to camp on the Reserve and, if so, is it desirable to concentrate camping on one suitable and properly equipped site? What signs, or notice boards are necessary? What should they say and where should they be placed? Is it necessary to make byelaws or to secure a Sanctuary Order under the Protection of Birds Act?

This by no means completes the picture of the problems which have to be faced in creating and managing Nature Reserves. No one appreciates having, say, polluted water running onto their ground, but in the case of Nature Reserves the scope for problems arising from inconvenient neighbours are much greater; industrial smoke even originating twenty or thirty miles distant may quite appreciably affect the flora and fauna. Again, quite distant drainage or water-pumping may lower the water table and make it difficult, expensive or even impossible to conserve aquatic plants and animals. Low flying, especially by jet aircraft or helicopters, may upset the birds and mammals.

The management of a Nature Reserve, therefore, requires close attention to developments on neighbouring land for a considerable distance around, which may well do more damage to the Reserve than any difficulties encountered inside it. It often happens that two or more inconsistent uses are proposed, either affecting the Reserve, or the neighbouring land, and the outcome is apt to be a compromise which is satisfactory neither for the Reserve nor for the other users concerned, but is inevitable in our overcrowded country.

While most Nature Reserves are chosen as being relatively undisturbed, a fair number derive their interest from past human interference ranging from ploughing in Neolithic times, to the operations of modern gravel-pits, sewage farms and reservoirs. Land apparently devastated by such agencies may, in time, acquire a special scientific value, especially if the process of colonisation following the disturbance is well documented.

In some cases it is not necessary for a Nature Reserve to be held exclusively for that purpose. A geological Reserve can perfectly well be combined, say, with a public open space or a sheep walk. A woodland Nature Reserve, held primarily for plants and insects, can be combined with sporting use. Coastal defence and water-gathering grounds are other uses which combine quite readily with nature conservation. Commercial timber production, and agriculture as distinct from live-stock-rearing, are among the uses which most often conflict, although, taking the country as a whole, the area of conflict is almost insignificant.

One of the most obstinate problems of vegetation control is the outcome of the reduced grazing of, for example, the chalk grasslands of south-eastern England. Without grazing the fine sward gives place first to coarse herbage, and before long to woody vegetation which develops into scrub and, if given long enough, into woodland. Unfortunately, this process involves not only the loss of pleasant views and pleasant places to walk about, but also the disappearance of interesting orchids, butterflies and other wild life which is attached to the chalk grassland. Economic difficulties and special problems such as worrying by dogs have discouraged farmers from rearing sheep which used to keep such areas grazed down, and the disappearance of rabbits from many of them following myxomatosis has temporarily aggravated the problem. Although any wild and undisturbed ground has its value for nature conservation, there can be little doubt that the increase of scrub woodland and thicket over so many of the remaining unreclaimed commons and heathlands of south-east England is a loss from the standpoint of wild life and it certainly leads to the increase of pests.

10. *Kingley Vale Nature Reserve. Aerial view with Yew Wood left and top. Wild clematis visible climbing yews in centre clump.*

11. *Bole of Yew Tree in the Kingley Vale Reserve.*

12. *Lullington Heath Nature Reserve. View from south-west looking along Oldkiln Bottom towards the Celtic fields, in the middle distance on left.*

In thoroughly natural conditions pests can hardly be said to exist, but the extent and unwisdom of human interference over the past two hundred years has created a very serious pest problem in Great Britain which no Nature Reserve management can ignore. The most promising remedy for this situation is to allow the natural predators, both birds and mammals, to regain their proper numbers and to play their useful role, but meanwhile it is undoubtedly necessary to repress such species as rats and carrion crows and in some cases the larger species of gulls.

Public activities on Nature Reserves also create many problems for the management. Many Nature Reserves are delightful places to which people naturally wish to have access for recreation and amenity and this is most desirable so long as their activities do not conflict with the main purpose for which the Nature Reserve exists. Everywhere there is the problem of the very small but highly destructive minority which starts fires, drops broken glass, uproots wild plants, defaces or destroys notices and interferes with scientific experiments and apparatus.

Unfortunately, however, it is not only this anti-social minority which injures Nature Reserves. Bird watchers who, forgetting that they are equipped with powerful binoculars, insist on approaching breeding or resting birds so near as to frighten them away, or botanists who collect large samples of the rarer vegetation, can be even more injurious. Many people again are slow to recognise that even a normally harmless activity, such as picking wild flowers, can be extremely inconvenient where the changes in the vegetation are being scientifically studied or where the wild flowers happen to be of a species which has been ex- terminated nearly everywhere else in the country. Sliding down sand dunes is great fun for the children, but less fun for the Reserve manage- ment which is confronted with blow-outs of drifting sand, possibly a hundred yards or more wide, resulting from an afternoon's amusement of this kind. Dog-lovers like to give their pets a bit of exercise, but hunting and terrifying the animals on Nature Reserves is not the most thoughtful way of doing it, nor are Nature Reserves proper places for cross-country motoring or motor-cycling, or for lighting bonfires or stoves. However, Nature Reserves are still a novelty and it is to be hoped that with the help of the Press, the B.B.C. and public opinion it will become better understood that public enjoyment of Nature Re- serves involves special restraint in the interests of the wild life and of the requirements of the scientific studies which have to be pursued on them. In one way or another the Nature Reserves will have to be assured of protection from human thoughtlessness.

D

Many people, even among those who visit and appreciate Nature Reserves, appear to assume that there is nothing which they can do about them. In fact, all sorts of people can do all sorts of things to help the Nature Reserves. Those who have special knowledge of some special group of animals and plants can help by volunteering to make surveys or lists of the group which they know about in Nature Reserves, where this information has not yet been recorded. Those who have a more general knowledge can still help in many cases if they are in a position to make simple regular observations, especially at Nature Reserves which have no full-time wardens. Again, most Nature Reserves are in great need of suitable honorary wardens who can help the regular warden out at peak visiting times, or act as substitutes when the warden is temporarily absent. Then, many people have special opportunities to educate visitors to Nature Reserves, for instance, through schools or clubs and societies or by making contacts in local hotels on such matters as those mentioned above.

Very often there is a good deal of straight-forward physical work to be done on Reserves in the way of cutting vegetation, keeping paths in good condition or helping to erect the signs, stiles and foot-bridges. Able-bodied volunteers for such work are usually welcome. Some wardens are inevitably lonely men and their interest and spirits are raised by an occasional word of appreciation and by passing on to them information which may be helpful to them in their duties. In these and other ways there is plenty of scope for those who are keen enough to help in running Britain's Nature Reserves.

BRITAIN'S NATURE RESERVES

Yarner Wood, Devon

NATURE CONSERVANCY RESERVE

2 miles west of Bovey Tracey: 352 acres. ACCESS. *Permits required
for whole Reserve*

YARNER WOOD in Devon is one of the richest of the Oak woodlands
flanking the high ground of Dartmoor. With its streams and
valleys, its steep slopes and plateaux and its wide variety of vegetation,
ranging from tall Oak forest to scrub Oak with much Holly and Rowan,
and with its fringe of heather moor and bog, it makes an ideal experimental area for the researches of the Nature Conservancy into management of semi-natural woodland. Yarner, like most surviving examples
of primeval woodland, has deteriorated very greatly through the centuries as a result of over-cutting of timber for construction and charcoal, over-grazing and browsing by intruding livestock, the indis-
criminate planting of alien species for amenity, and a great deal of
general neglect, culminating in a disastrous fire in 1942, when the Ger-
man Luftwaffe unloaded over the centre of the wood a large quantity of
incendiary bombs which were doubtless intended for some other target.

Although so varied, the wood contains no rarities and can therefore
be used for scientific experiments without fear of doing harm to scarce
species. Basic experiments are designed to ensure that enough trees of
native species are able to grow successfully to their full stature to re-
place in due course the largely distorted and degenerate existing specimens and to bring the whole wood up to the standard of the best surviving parts of it, where some tall and well-grown Oaks and other trees
show what the wood might be like. Experimental plots are small,
mostly of half an acre or an acre, and are planted on an elaborate
plan to test out the capabilities of the different trees, particularly Oak,
Beech and Alder, and also to compare the results of planting in cleared
areas as against planting under the existing canopy or relying on natural
regeneration, which has in modern times been rather poor. Other
experiments include the intensive provision of nesting boxes for woodland insect-eating birds and these have resulted in immediate colonisa-

tion by Pied Flycatchers, which have never within human memory or record had a breeding colony so far south in England. Buzzards, Ravens and all three species of Woodpeckers are among the other nesting birds. Geologically, the Reserve is just off the edge of the Dartmoor granite and consists almost entirely of Culm measures of carboniferous age. The granite for building London Bridge (1825-31) was brought out from Hay Tor down a mineral railway which ran through Yarner Wood.

According to local legend Yarner Wood is a favourite hiding place of the Devil, but scientific confirmation of this is not so far forthcoming.

Axmouth-Lyme Regis Undercliffs, Devon

NATURE CONSERVANCY RESERVE

Between Seaton and Lyme Regis: 794 acres. Part owned, part leased and part under Nature Reserve Agreement with Major O. Allhusen. ACCESS. *By public footpaths; permits required elsewhere*

Most Nature Reserves owe their value to having been comparatively undisturbed for a very long time. These Undercliffs by contrast are interesting because of their extreme geological instability, vividly illustrated by the aerial photograph on page 18. The chasm shown, which is half a mile long, about 100-200 feet deep and 200-400 feet wide, was created at Dowlands on Christmas Day, 1839, when nearly eight million tons of Chalk and Upper Greensand rock became detached from the cliff, and slipped seawards down the gently sloping underlying Gault and Lias beds. The cause was almost certainly prolonged excessive rainfall which washed out much of the intervening Foxmould sands and converted the rest into a quicksand unable to drain off through the impervious layers beneath. Thus undermined and underlubricated the great cliff moved like a ship being launched sideways.

There had been some settlement earlier, but it was only on returning from the traditional burning of the ashen faggot at 1 a.m. on Christmas Day that William Pritchard and his wife found that the ground on the way home had sunk a foot. At 3 a.m. he and his neighbours had to evacuate their houses hurriedly. A contemporary account in the *Penny Magazine* reported 'rocks rent asunder . . . trees uprooted, and the ruins of two cottages which stood in the midst, altogether form a scene of wilderness, desolation and grandeur, at once awful and sublime.' The chasm was estimated to have swallowed about 27 acres of tillage

13. *Dungeness Nature Reserve. Aerial view showing Bird Observatory (arrowed) and lighthouse to right. Shingle ridges eroded at near ends trace successive former coastlines, most of right-hand half having been added in recent centuries.*

14. *Another aerial view of the Dungeness Reserve looking south with Hoppen Pits in the centre.*

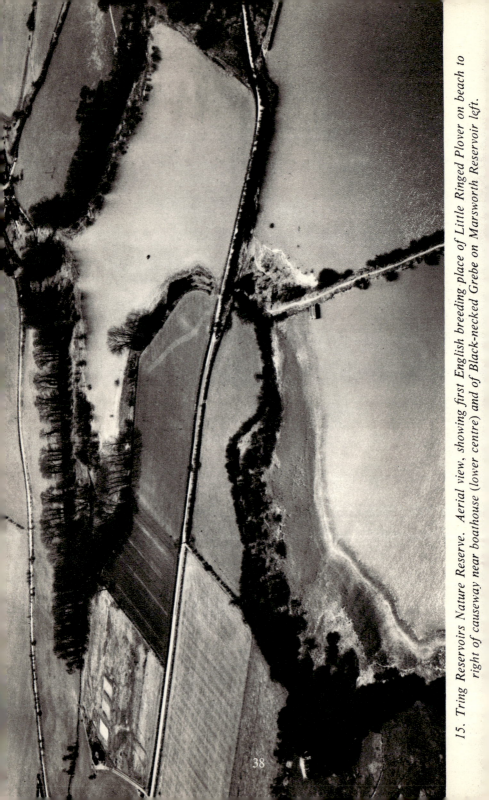

15. *Tring Reservoirs Nature Reserve. Aerial view, showing first English breeding place of Little Ringed Plover on beach to right of causeway near boathouse (lower centre) and of Black-necked Grebe on Marsworth Reservoir left.*

16. *Black-necked Grebe approaching its nest on Marsworth Reservoir, Tring, in 1919, a year after breeding in England was first recorded there.*

17. *Wychwood Nature Reserve. View along ride looking south-west. On both sides are fifty-year-old plantations of Beech, Elm, Chestnut, Sycamore and Ash on ancient woodland soil.*

land, but nearly 13 acres, still divided by a hedge, carried the turnips and young wheat recently sown on them and the wheat was duly harvested in its new situation on August 25, 1840, in the presence of over ten thousand spectators and with the assistance of young ladies dressed as Nymphs of Ceres.

The fact that the President of the Geological Society happened to be spending that Christmas at Lyme Regis helped to ensure that ample records, surveys and drawings were taken, and these show how valuable such things can be a hundred years afterwards. Mary Buckland's sketches, made within a week of the event, illustrate it most vividly and these, with photographs extending back over fifty years, enable us to see how nearly treeless was the chasm and the detached cliff, not only in 1839 but as recently as 1905. The great majority of the trees visible in the aerial view are under fifty years old, yet this Ash-wood is wholly natural, and is one of the few natural woods whose entire evolution and history can be traced, which adds much to its scientific interest. Migratory insects and birds also reach the Undercliffs in some numbers, but they have not yet been sufficiently studied. A Hoopoe was reported in 1956.

While there are no especially rare breeding birds this is one of the few places which attracts both south-eastern woodland species such as the Nightingale and Nuthatch and western cliff breeders such as the Raven, Buzzard and Herring-Gull.

This Nature Reserve is also interesting because it extends over six miles and thus forms the longest stretch of the English coast to be safeguarded from all development as Crown Land under the National Parks and Access to the Countryside Act, 1949. It is also the most important coastal landslip area in Great Britain and includes one of the largest areas of absolutely natural vegetation and largely undisturbed cover for animals in England. Visitors are asked to keep to the public footpath: to visit the remainder of the Reserve requires not only a permit but considerable strength and energy.

Bridgwater Bay, Somerset

NATURE CONSERVANCY RESERVE

12 miles south of Weston-super-Mare: 6,000 acres. Under Nature Reserve Agreement with Somerset River Board. ACCESS. *Permits required for Steart Island; unrestricted elsewhere*

UP THE Bristol Channel run some of the strongest and highest tides in the whole world, and at Bridgwater Bar, just below the narrowing of the funnel to form the Severn Estuary, the rise of Spring Tides is as high as 35 feet, compared with under seven feet at Lowestoft and nine feet at Portland Bill. Here at the mouth of the River Parrett is a great expanse of mud flats which are rapidly covered by each rising tide leaving very little of the Bridgwater Bay Nature Reserve above water. For every square foot of bottom covered to a depth of six feet it has been calculated that there are four ounces of mud in suspension in the sea water, and advantage has been taken of this to experiment empirically over the past 30 years by planting the hybrid Cord Grass (*Spartina townsendii*), whose stiff brown stems trap the mud and build up the level of the coast line. From a single lorry-load brought from Poole Harbour about 1928 this plant has now densely covered an area about one and a half miles long and about 200 yards wide, and is estimated to have raised the level in places by as much as two to three feet.

Following the suggestions of the Waverley Departmental Committee on Coastal Flooding, the Conservancy, in conjunction with the Somerset River Board, are undertaking a good deal of experimental work on the properties of Cord Grass as a builder of silt for flood prevention, and on the local movements of beach materials and trends in erosion and deposition. About 1,200 markers, graded in size to conform to the natural beach material, were laid down in the Reserve, each marker carrying a tag to indicate its point of origin and the state of the tide at which it had been placed there. Observations showed that the Cord Grass patches were very effective in checking the drift and giving rise to shingle ridges at their western end. The shingle bank thus formed eventually brings destruction to the Cord Grass, suddenly overwhelming it.

Ornithologically, Bridgwater Bay Nature Reserve is important partly because it is the only known British moulting area for Shelduck, several thousands of which gather there annually around July while most of the remaining British population fly over to the Heligoland Bight to join Shelduck from Germany, Holland and other Western European countries. In winter large numbers of waders and some wild geese, chiefly White-fronted, frequent the flats, and it is one of the few places where the Avocet is often seen outside the breeding season. Wintering Short-eared Owls are fond of hunting over the salt marshes. Steart Island, off the mouth of the river Parrett, became separated from the mainland about the end of the 18th century, although its breeding shore birds and Terns have been reduced to insignificant numbers.

Part of the Nature Reserve consists of the newly constructed New Huntspill River, which should allow valuable experience to be gained about the conservation possibilities of the growing number of civil engineering works concerned either with water supply, flood control, or drainage. It is difficult and sometimes dangerous to go out across the mud, but by the intelligent use of good binoculars or telescopes the whole area can be well observed by birdwatchers without disturbing the feeding and resting birds, especially when the tide is about at half ebb.

Steep Holm, Somerset

STEEP HOLM TRUST RESERVE

In Bristol Channel, 5 miles west of Weston-super-Mare. 63 acres. ACCESS. *Restricted*

STEEP HOLM is a rocky island something over half a mile long and 300 yards broad rising 250 feet out of the Bristol Channel, five miles west of Weston-super-Mare in Somerset, and about the same distance south-east from the Glamorganshire coast. The rock is Carboniferous Limestone. The sister island of Flat Holm lies $2\frac{1}{4}$ miles to the north-north-west.

The island was a victim of one of the earlier war scares and was heavily fortified in 1867 with gun batteries which involved a great deal of excavation, while barracks and a powder house still survive from this project.

Steep Holm has always been of great interest to naturalists and in 1954 the Steep Holm Trust was formed by the collaboration of the Somerset Archaeological and Natural History Society, the Bristol Naturalists' Society, the Mid-Somerset Naturalists' Society and the

Bristol Folk House Archaeological Club. Among the Trust's objects is the preservation of the bird life, including the colonies of Gulls and Cormorants, and the breeding places of the Shelduck, Peregrine and Raven. The Steep Holm Trust Gull Research Station has now been established, controlled by a specially appointed Research Committee and recognised by the British Trust for Ornithology. The flora includes the rare Wild Peony (*Paeonia mascula*), the Wild Leek (*Allium ampeloprasm*), and the Golden Samphire (*Inula crithmoides*).

The island has been uninhabited for some years and is sometimes impossible to approach or leave in bad weather. It is not unknown for parties to be marooned there. The Trust has had a very heavy task in getting the accommodation into habitable order after the disruption caused by re-fortification in the Second World War; and also in clearing vegetation for the benefit of the Wild Peony which in 1914 was reported as barely surviving. It responded in a remarkable way and is now flourishing in a number of places on the island. Apart from Elder, Privet and some Sycamore, the densest vegetation consists of Alexanders or Horse Parsley (*Smyrnium olusatrum*), which was first recorded there by Turner in 1568 and which covered most of the island a few years ago, forming a meadow on the top plateau which was botanically unique. The Wild Peony, which is found nowhere else in Britain, is believed to have been introduced by the monks. The Wild Leek, although first recorded in 1625, is probably also an introduction. Some 261 species of flowering plants and ferns have been recorded on this small area, and the present flora is estimated at about 225.

Among birds, the Herring Gulls and Lesser Black-backed Gulls are dominant. In 1902 there were only about 25 pairs of Herring Gulls and a few of Lesser Black-backs. When the island became uninhabited in 1922 there was a rapid increase in two years to about 100 pairs of Lesser Black-backs and about 150 pairs of Herring Gulls. By 1933 there were estimated to be about 500 pairs of Lesser Black-backed Gulls out of a total of 1,200 of the two species combined. A census in 1956 found 3,500 nests of Herring Gulls, 625 of Lesser Black-backed Gulls and 74 of Great Black-backs. It is claimed that this was the largest single breeding colony of Herring Gulls in the British Isles. The Great Black-backed Gull, which was exterminated as a breeding species about the mid-nineteenth century, began to breed again in 1923 and is also increasing. Cormorants, first recorded as nesting in 1934, breed on the north side cliffs—a colony of 20-30 pairs.

In spite of the legacy of its military use, Steep Holm retains consider-

18. *Wychwood Nature Reserve. Aerial view of semi-natural woodland in ancient forest.*

19. *The same Reserve. View northwards up Evenden Bottom from point just above the Cyder Well. Main species of tree are Pedunculate Oak, Field Maple, Hawthorn and Elder forming natural graduated woodland edge.*

45

20. Minsmere Level. Aerial view showing shallow brackish waters, marshes and sea-shore at top, scene of successive inbreaks by North Sea. (The Tree Hide is at extreme right of crescent-shaped belt of trees.)

21. Entering Tree Hide at Minsmere Level.

able botanical and ornithological interest and is a good example of concerted effort by a number of local societies with the backing of a University to conserve and undertake research on a site of much scientific interest. Such efforts are a very necessary complement to the national programme of Nature Reserves.

Fyfield Down, Wiltshire

NATURE CONSERVANCY RESERVE

3 miles west of Marlborough: 612 acres. Leased from the owner, Mr G. E. Todd. ACCESS. *By public footpaths; permits required elsewhere*

CHALK is the backbone of the most characteristic scenery of Southern England and the great chalk hills radiate from the uplands centred on Salisbury Plain. On these uplands, during the Eocene period, was deposited a bed of sand whose only contents are a few roots and stems of plants. Part of the sand became hardened into rock, and when later on the soft sands were all denuded away the hardened portions remained as extremely durable boulders, called Sarsens, the greatest surviving clusters of which are in the area between Avebury and Marlborough in Wiltshire. Here probably the earliest British civilisation grew up, at the crossroads between the Ridge Way coming down from the Chilterns and the Berkshire Downs to Salisbury Plain and the Herepath coming from the east. Here was practised some of the earliest British agriculture. From hereabouts also were brought the great megaliths for Avebury, the first important architectural monument in Britain. If there is any region which can be called the birthplace of British civilisation, this is it.

Since prehistoric times these downlands have changed from being one of the most populated parts of southern Britain to being among the least disturbed, until very recent years when the bulldozer and other heavy equipment has made it possible to reclaim even land thickly peppered with the great Sarsen stones. To avert their threatened disappearance from the plateau land the Nature Conservancy in 1955 established the Nature Reserve of Fyfield Down, straddling the Herepath immediately to the east of its crossing of the Ridge Way.

The Grey Wethers (as the Sarsens are locally known from their sheep-like appearance) lie thick not only in the hollows but even on the plateau

E

land where the outlines of the Neolithic field system can still be clearly made out. These relics of our earliest farms, which went out of cultivation probably about the close of the Romano-British period, have left interesting effects on the soil and consequently on the flora and fauna. At the same time the gradual weathering of the Sarsen stones has created pockets of acid soils on which grow acid-loving plants such as Sheep's Sorrel and Heath Bedstraw in the middle of the chalk downland with its lime-loving characteristic plants.

There is an interesting and varied moss flora associated with the sandstones. The highest point on the Reserve is about 830 feet. More than 60 breeding species of birds have recently been listed including the Wheatear, Grasshopper Warbler and six species of tits. The Hen Harrier, Buzzard, Peregrine, Quail, Hoopoe, and Short-eared and Long-eared Owl have also been observed.

The Reserve is grazed by sheep and is used partly for exercising racehorses in accordance with local tradition which helps to ensure that the fine downland turf will be maintained, in contrast to the large areas where it has recently either been destroyed by the plough or become overgrown with scrub. The Brome Grass (*Zerna erecta*) and Sheep's Fescue are dominant over most of the down, but in the neighbourhood of the Sarsens, Heath Bedstraw (*Galium hercynicum*) and occasionally Ling become prominent. Meadow Saxifrage (*Saxifraga granulata*) is a notable feature of the flora, although no really rare plants have been found.

Fyfield Down Reserve was originally recommended on strictly geological grounds, but its botanical, ornithological and archaeological interests are proving increasingly important as so many other characteristic stretches of the chalk downland vanish under reclamation.

Old Winchester Hill, Hampshire

NATURE CONSERVANCY RESERVE

2½ miles south of West Meon between Petersfield and Winchester:
140 acres. ACCESS. *Unrestricted*

IT SEEMS only yesterday since the short springy turf of the chalk downlands extended almost unbroken from Winchester over Butser Hill and along the South Downs to Beachy Head, some 70 miles distant. All the way were reminders of some of the earliest human communities of Southern England, and at intervals the characteristic chalk herbage was varied by unexpected patches of heather, where the chalk was capped with shallow deposits of acid clay soil.

One of the best of these was adjoining the fine Iron Age camp on Old Winchester Hill which commands the Upper Meon Valley, between Winchester and Petersfield. Unfortunately, although this interesting area survived the war, it fell a victim to agricultural reclamation shortly before steps could be taken to acquire it for scientific study and nature conservation. The Nature Conservancy were, however, successful in 1954 in acquiring the Hill itself as a National Nature Reserve. In spite of its fairly small size—140 acres—this Reserve has a great variety of aspects, as the hill slopes steeply away from the camp to the south, to the west and to the north and north-east. Most of it is rough chalk grassland, but there are patches of well-grown Yew and other chalk-loving trees. On the southern slopes there is a good growth of Juniper, which has become uncommon since so much chalk downland has been reclaimed for agriculture since the beginning of the Second World War. On the brows facing towards the south-west the soil has been leached so that the Ling, which needs acid conditions, has been able to invade the chalk grassland.

Unfortunately, the Hill has not been grazed recently, except by rabbits, which largely disappeared as a result of myxomatosis in 1955. Their disappearance helped to check erosion in the neighbourhood of their warrens and to permit an exceptional flowering of orchids and other attractive plants, but it aggravated the invasion by Hawthorns and other woody vegetation which are rapidly encroaching on the grass-land, creating a problem for management.

This is one of the Reserves on which transects have been set up to be regularly observed in order to trace changes in the composition of vegetation, particularly those resulting from myxomatosis and the disappearance of rabbits. The recent improvements of road access have brought large numbers of visitors in cars. The use of the Reserve by picnickers, gypsies and for military training has created considerable problems, as people find it difficult to realise that such activities as driving cars over the grass, pulling up moss or cutting off branches of trees can interfere very seriously with important scientific studies. Stone Curlews used to breed on the Hill, but it is now far too much disturbed for them to continue doing so.

Kingley Vale, Sussex

NATURE CONSERVANCY RESERVE

4 miles north-west of Chichester: 230 *acres.* ACCESS. *Unrestricted*

YEWS are among the most impressive and characteristic trees of the chalk downlands of Southern England. Those at Kingley Vale, four miles north-west of Chichester on the Sussex Downs, have long been celebrated as possibly the finest yew wood in all Europe. The age of the Yews is a subject of controversy, but many of them are very large and the shade which they cast is so deep that hardly anything will grow underneath them. They are, however, interspersed with the equally lime-loving Ash, Whitebeam and Juniper, especially on the very steep south-facing and east-facing slopes of the coomb, which used to be called Kingley Bottom.

The summit ridge of the Reserve, along Bow Hill, reaches 655 feet above sea-level and carries some very fine tumuli, sometimes called 'the Tumps', which can be seen for a great distance on the skyline. On this ridge also is a well-developed acid heath of Ling and other typical species occupying the loamy-flinty clay soil of the plateau, which contrasts markedly with the surrounding chalk flora. This contrast adds to the scientific value of the area for studying the distribution of species which are restricted to either calcareous or acid soils. The loam on the plateau has recently become overgrown with Hawthorn and other bushes and some of the Yews have been almost smothered by Clematis and Brambles. On the whole, however, the vegetation can be left to look after itself.

Apart from the patch of clay with flints on the north ridge, the Reserve lies mainly on the Upper Chalk with a large area of Coombe Rock in the valley towards the south. Although Stone Curlews have long nested in the neighbourhood the bird life of the Reserve is not particularly remarkable.

Lullington Heath, Sussex

NATURE CONSERVANCY RESERVE

3½ *miles north-west of Seaford: 155 acres. Held under lease.*
ACCESS. *By public footpaths; permits required elsewhere*

SHORTLY after the Second World War nearly all the surviving tracts of heather on the chalk downlands were destroyed by ploughing for agricultural reclamation to assist the temporary national food difficulties following the cancellation of Lease-Lend. One characteristic area just over three miles north-west of Seaford escaped this fate by being earmarked for afforestation. When the Forestry Commission learned of the destruction of the other examples of this habitat, they generously relinquished their prior claims in the interests of ecological research and in July, 1956, the area was declared a National Nature Reserve.

Prehistoric farmers have left their mark on it, as the boundaries of their rectangular fields can still be traced and fragments of pottery and iron slag show that people lived and worked here too. Far from reducing the biological value of the Reserve, these traces of long-past soil disturbance add to its interest and provide a link with agricultural history. Cultivation seems to have ceased many hundreds of years ago, and although the chalk lies only a few inches below the surface, the lime has been leached from the soil which is now acid and accordingly favours shallow-rooted plants such as Bell Heather which like acid conditions, while mingled with them are deeper-rooted plants such as Salad Burnet and Dropwort which need a limy soil. The Reserve contains *Erica* heath side by side with chalk grassland and also Gorse and Hawthorn scrub; it also has two Badger setts.

Lullington Heath is the scene of some of the most important long-term survey work to determine what are the full effects of the disappearance of the rabbits following myxomatosis and these effects will, of course, be of importance whether the rabbits ultimately recolonise or not, since it is improbable that their numbers and position in the balance of nature will revert to what they were before they received this fearful blow. At Lullington Heath there is the special factor that forestry plantations are beginning to grow up on most of the surrounding downland and the Reserve will become increasingly cut off by these and by agriculture from other reservoirs of the wild life of the chalk grasslands and heaths.

The area leased by the Nature Conservancy is owned by the East-bourne Waterworks Company, and both water gathering and scientific research requirements necessitate access being kept to a minimum, although the Reserve can be well seen from the public trackway which crosses it.

Dungeness, Kent

ROYAL SOCIETY FOR THE PROTECTION OF BIRDS RESERVE

About 4 miles south-east of Lydd: 1,243 acres. ACCESS. *By public rights of way; restricted elsewhere*

NO OTHER square mile of Britain has been created by nature so recently as the Point of Dungeness. As near as Shakespeare's time the coast was probably a mile farther back than the Point as we know it to-day. Not so many centuries earlier the waves came right up to the face of the former sea-cliffs which can still be seen, many miles inland fronting the Royal Military Canal behind Romney Marsh. At some later stage a long shingle bank seems to have formed from the cliffs off Fairlight, north-eastwards through New Romney to Hythe near Folkestone, shutting in a great flat area which we now know as Romney Marsh.

A projecting ness seems to have developed on this straight shingle coastline somewhere in Rye Bay and gradually to have been pushed farther eastwards until in Saxon times it may have been just south of the Open Pits or Hoppen Pits. These are the only freshwater lagoons of any size over shingle beach anywhere in Britain, and Dungeness itself is the most important tract of shingle. Its impressiveness is heightened by the fact that the 10-fathom line runs only a few hundred yards off the Point, and a continuous procession of deep-sea ships goes past up and down the Channel bearing witness to the tremendous size of the structure, almost entirely of flint pebbles, which has been raised here from the floor of the English Channel.

Dungeness is above all a natural monument, and research on its evolution may prove a key to processes of coastal erosion and to rises and falls in the sea level. Many of the shingle ridges have been damaged or destroyed by military explosive trials, gravel working or development, and the preservation of the remainder is due more than anything else to the efforts of a few ornithologists, including the late R. B. Burrowes, who by his persistence and his personal financial generosity did more than anyone else to secure the area of the Dungeness Nature Reserve, covering a large expanse of shingle running westwards from the Coastguard Station.

During the Second World War the whole Reserve was occupied by the military and suffered so heavily that serious doubts were felt regarding the possibility of its recovery. However, in 1952 the Nature Conservancy made a grant to the Royal Society for the Protection of Birds to employ a full-time watcher, Mr. H. E. Axell, in order to experiment with various methods of management which might restore the Reserve to its former importance.

The small colony of Common Gulls breeding at Dungeness are 300 miles farther south than any other of this species in Britain, and the Herring Gull colony is probably the only important colony in Britain on shingle. Neither of these had been able to rear any young for several years and the Terns were equally hard pressed. In 1952, under protection, 26 pairs of Common Terns bred and there were similar numbers in the next three years, but the breeding success was disappointing. Carrion Crows, Hedgehogs, Foxes and other predators took a heavy toll. Much valuable experience was gained, however, and 170 species of birds were seen on or from the Reserve between April, 1952, and 1955. Immediately adjoining the Reserve, the Dungeness Bird Observatory was also established in 1952 and in the first two years of its operation nearly 7,000 birds of about 100 species were ringed.

The colonisation of plants over the shingle is ecologically most interesting and Dungeness is the home of a number of extremely rare species, including one probably extinct everywhere else in Britain, and several which occur nowhere else in Kent. Dungeness is also very favourable for insects, including migratory species which sometimes occur in large numbers. Few of Britain's Nature Reserves can look more bleak and unprepossessing, but few contain a wider variety of scientific interest.

Tring Reservoirs, Hertfordshire

NATURE CONSERVANCY RESERVE

49 acres. Held under lease. ACCESS. *By rights of way; permits required elsewhere*

EXPANSES of fresh water can be equally attractive to birds and to other mobile animals whether they are natural or are artificially created. The Tring Reservoirs were formed in the first years of the nineteenth century to serve the Grand Junction Canal, now renamed the Grand Union Canal. They lie nearly on the 400 foot contour, and can thus maintain water in both the sections of the Canal running down from Tring summit towards London and towards Birmingham. However, with the more powerful modern pumps their importance to the operation of the Canal is considerably reduced and for some years after the Second World War they were partially by-passed, thus allowing the water to drop to very low levels, with unfortunate effects on the bird and plant life, and in the encouragement of increased disturbance by the public.

Being an artificially created and artificially maintained habitat, the reservoirs are to some extent at the mercy of the future economic and technical conditions for canal operation. In 1955 the banks of all four reservoirs—Wilstone, Marsworth, Little Tring and Startopsend—were constituted a Nature Reserve by the Nature Conservancy with the co-operation of the British Transport Commission and of Lord Rothschild.

Their attractions to ornithologists are such that those responsible for recording the birds of Hertfordshire have criticised their correspondents for concentrating so heavily on Tring at the expense of all other parts of the county. In 1918 the Black-necked Grebe bred at Marsworth Reservoir for the first time on record in England, and in 1938 the adjoining Startopsend Reservoir attracted to its dry bank the first pair of Little Ringed Plovers ever known to nest in Britain. While, unfortunately, neither species has continued to breed regularly at Tring, both have become well established as British breeding birds. The reservoirs, lying roughly midway between the Wash and Southampton Water, attract large numbers of migrating waterfowl, waders, gulls and terns, including a number of rarities, such as in September, 1953, the American Lesser Yellowlegs. Nesting duck include Pochard, Tufted Duck, Shoveler and Teal, and the Garganey has also bred there.

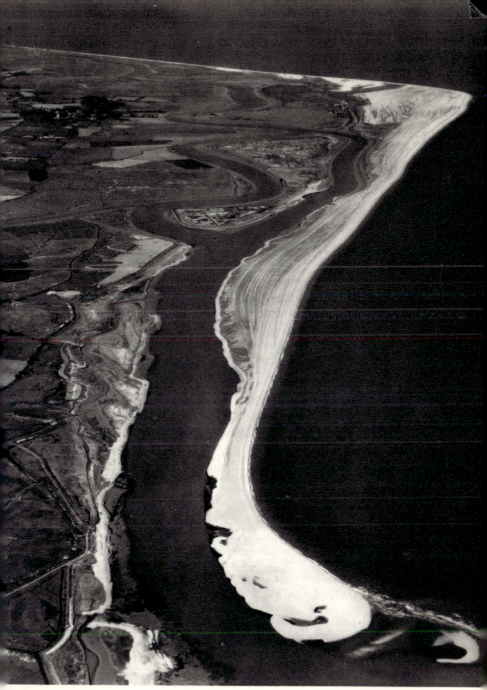

22. *Orfordness-Havergate Nature Reserve. Aerial view. The Reserve consists of Havergate Island (above right centre) and the shingle spit from near the river bend opposite the north-east end of the island to North Weir Point near centre of foreground. Nearly all was submerged on January 31, 1953.*

55

23. *Hickling Broad.
Aerial view showing
Whiteslea Lodge
(left) and sailing
channel to Heigham
Sound.*

The marshy ground (which existed here even before the reservoirs) provides a habitat for some locally rate plants such as the Round-fruited Rush (*Juncus compressus*), the Orange Foxtail (*Alopecurus equalis*) and the Broadleaved Ragwort (*Senecio fluviatilis*). The reservoirs also have a number of interesting records for insects, including the only occurrence in Hertfordshire of the large and handsome American Milkweed Butterfly (*Danaus plexippus*), which was seen between the Canal and the reservoirs in August, 1947.

Several well-known naturalists, including the late Lord Rothschild, the late Charles Oldham and Julian Huxley have made observations at Tring. The reservoirs are also famous among anglers.

Wytham Woods, Berkshire

OXFORD UNIVERSITY ESTATE
INCLUDING SCIENTIFIC RESERVES

5½ miles from Oxford: c. 1,000 acres. ACCESS. *Restricted*

So MANY obscure animals and plants inhabit Great Britain that, apart from a few small barren islands, there is no area in the country whose animals and plants are known even sufficiently to make a list of them. Before we can begin to understand ecology, or the relationships of animals and plants to their environment and to one another, it is essential that we should be able to trace the entire fauna and flora of at least a small number of small areas, and to work out why they are there and what they are doing. This calls for the collaboration of a considerable number of specialists with laboratories, museums and libraries behind them. It is a task which takes many years to complete and the attempt could be frustrated if the area under study were interfered with before the study was completed. A long-term assurance of security for the area is, therefore, essential to such a programme.

The only place in Britain where such a continuing survey is at present being carried out on a large scale is on the estate of Wytham, close to Oxford, which came into the possession of the University through the generosity of Colonel ffennell. The estate covers about five square miles and includes about a thousand acres of woodlands and parkland, together with more than two thousand acres of grassland, arable and river levels adjoining the River Isis, which forms the northern and

F

north-east boundary; the main road from Swinford to Botley near Oxford forms the southern boundary.

This sizeable area is a typical but rather rich sample of south Midland country on calcareous soils. About a tenth of the central thousand acres has been set aside by the University as scientific reserves, in the form of small pieces of woodland, scrub, limestone grassland, marsh, pond and stream. These are specially protected, but field research is done also on the rest of the woodlands, which are managed by the Department of Forestry. On the latter some smaller sites, such as logs, are specially marked and preserved for research.

Since about 1945 the Bureau of Animal Population, Department of Zoological Field Studies, has organized an ecological survey system under C. S. Elton, for keeping track of the results of the large stream of investigation being done by its own members, and also by the Edward Grey Institute, the Hope Department of Entomology, and other University bodies. These comprise many independent pieces of research, on small mammals, birds, insects and other invertebrates, living in a variety of habitats. Already at least 2,500 species of animals are known to live on the area. The vegetation has been less intensively studied, but a great deal is known from the incidental records of the Forestry Department and the Bureau of Animal Population.

The trapping alive, marking and recapturing of mice and voles has occupied some Bureau workers over the last ten years. H. N. Southern's study of the numbers and food of the Tawny Owl at Wytham is one of the most complete yet made for any bird of prey; while elaborate observations of Titmouse populations have been made by J. Gibb, P. H. T. Hartley and others. Research on invertebrates covers dozens of projects including those by G. C. Varley on Oakmoths, C. S. Elton on Ash Bark-beetles, A. Macfadyen and C. Overgaard Nielson on the limestone soil and litter system, and E. W. Fager on the fauna of small logs.

Geologically the ground is varied, as the lower slopes are Oxford Clay, an intermediate narrow band of Corallian sands, and the cap a limestone Coral Rag reef which rises to 539 feet and has a few traces of glacial drift in places.

Wytham contains a variety of interesting species. There is a rich limestone flora resembling that of chalk grassland. The geological zonation produces many small springs and marshes below the sand, while the sand itself contains badger earths. But the chief scientific value is that the whole area can be used for ecological survey, measurements and experiments—like the Waterperry Forest Nature Reserve in

24. *Marsh Harrier at its nest.*

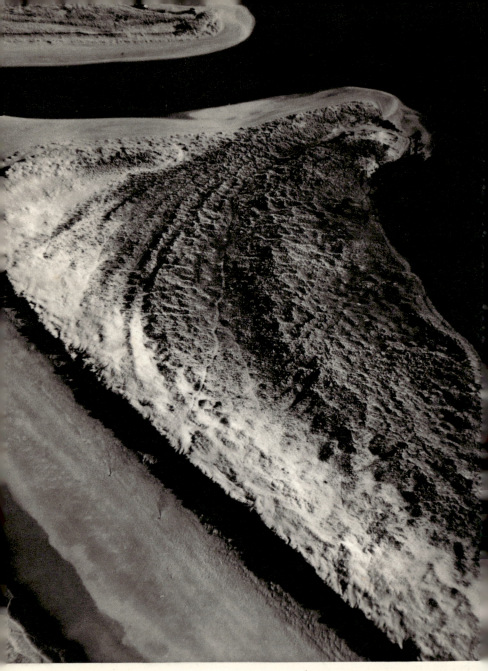

25. *Scolt Head Nature Reserve. The east end from the air, showing dark shadow of front ridge of dunes on Plantago Marsh undergoing marine erosion, with Burnham Harbour and Gun Hill in background.*

Bernwood Forest set aside by the Forestry Commission in agreement with the Nature Conservancy early in 1954 to enable research to be done by scientists from Oxford and elsewhere. A complementary picture of more natural woodland conditions is afforded by the Nature Conservancy Reserve at Wychwood, separately described, which lies about eight miles to the north-west.

Wychwood, Oxfordshire

NATURE CONSERVANCY RESERVE

About 7 miles west of Woodstock: 647 acres. Under Nature Reserve Agreement with Mr Oliver Watney. ACCESS. Permits required for whole Reserve

WHEN in 1955 the Nature Conservancy in agreement with the owner, Mr Oliver Watney, declared Wychwood Forest a National Nature Reserve, they were in a sense only redefining in modern terms the purposes which had been pretty consistently pursued by successive kings, keepers and proprietors of Wychwood since the Norman Conquest. The square mile which has survived to become a Nature Reserve is, however, only a tiny fragment of the original forest stretching from Burford to Woodstock and Witney. It represents only about one-sixth of the woodland area which survived up to about a hundred years ago when it was disafforested and two-thirds of it were grubbed up.

Over the centuries the natural woodland has suffered severely. The vegetation survey completed by the Nature Conservancy in 1954 was only the latest of a series of official records going back more than 800 years and this rich documentation about past human interference adds to the scientific value of the Reserve. We know, for instance, about firewood and charcoal being taken from the forest as long ago as 1206, the taking of wild boars and the unauthorised incursions of pigs shortly afterwards, and Henry III's instructions regarding timber blown over by the great gale of 1222. We know that timber extraction was very active at this period and that the men of several neighbouring villages were allowed to keep goats in the forest until the King directed otherwise. There was trouble in 1271 about the forest being torn up by hogs, but Edward I was able to make large gifts both of timber, firewood and deer. A tale of damage to the forest by unauthorised timber-cutting and grazing continues through the centuries and in 1636 there is an interesting record of damage being done by rabbits to the vert during the past ten years. This damage seems to have grown worse under Cromwell, but the rabbits evidently did not prevent the success of the tree-planting programme undertaken for Lord Clarendon by John Evelyn, the founder of English silviculture. However, by the late eighteenth century things became so bad that (as the Commissioners appointed by Parliament reported) 'little chance remains of any succession of timber in this forest unless some change of management shall take place'. They added that about a thousand deer were damaging the trees and underwood, that no timber had been supplied for the navy for nearly a hundred years, that the cover for young wood growing up is destroyed by lopping and cutting, and that the forest is overrun by swine. (According to other evidence there were about this time three or four men in gaol at Oxford for deer-stealing in the forest.)

During the nineteenth century damage by deer and by human trespassers was got under control, but successive attacks of rabbits, grey squirrels and, since the Second World War, more deer which strayed in during military occupation of the neighbouring park, led to a further almost total check to regeneration of the woodland, and to the drawing up of the present silvicultural plan to enable it to recover with the absolute minimum of human and other disturbance.

Wychwood was worked botanically by John Blackstone 220 years ago. It was Lord Denby, Ranger of Wychwood Forest, who founded the earliest botanic garden in Britain at Oxford in 1621, and Oxford's first Professor of Botany, Dillenius, was collecting in Wychwood more than 200 years ago plants all of which can still be found there with the one sad exception of the lovely Pasque Flower (*Anemone pulsatilla*). Other Oxford Professors and research workers have continued to investigate Wychwood at intervals from that time until this.

Wychwood is primarily an Oak and Ash forest with an under-storey of Hawthorn, including the local *Crataegus oxyacanthoides*, Hazel and Field Maple, which was used for making flagons for the Plantagenets. There are no birds of special interest. The abundance of Roman Snails (*Helix pomatia*) is a conspicuous feature.

Wychwood has extremely interesting geological features since it was apparently very close to the maximum southward extension of the Ice Cap. It lies on the great Oolite limestone plateau, but is traversed by a steep-sided valley which cuts down to the upper Lias Clay and is largely capped by a grey acid clay. The Forest Marble Beds, named from Wychwood, crop out in certain places.

Wychwood provides a fascinating if fragmentary example of many of the main elements in the pattern of nature conservation and research and experiment in ecology in Great Britain. It is to be hoped that over the next fifty years the elements can be brought together and the pattern can be viewed as a whole.

Minsmere Level, Suffolk

ROYAL SOCIETY FOR THE PROTECTION OF BIRDS RESERVE

3 miles south of Dunwich: 1,600 acres. Held under lease.
ACCESS. *Permits to visit obtainable from R.S.P.B.*

SUFFOLK, which projects farther east into the North Sea than any other county, is deeply penetrated at its south-eastern corner by the broad tidal estuaries of the rivers Stour, Orwell, Deben, Alde and Blyth. As a result, both the railway and the main road parallel with the coast run several miles away inland, thus keeping down the seaside traffic and population to a fairly low level. Between Felixstowe and Southwold the recent geological deposits brought down the former course of the Rhine give rise to a highly varied landscape of gravel and sandy ridges alternating with fertile land and low marshes, and carrying a rich range of heather and woodland, meres and reedbeds, streams, cliffs, sands and shingle, which cover most of the possible habitat types for many different plants and animals.

This quiet and favoured littoral has long been in the hands of a number of enlightened land-owning families who have cared for it and its wild life so well as to make it a sportsman's model nature reserve. Owing to these unusual advantages it is possible normally to see in a given time something like one-third more species of birds in this part of Suffolk than anywhere else in the British Isles. Along this favoured coast the richest concentrations of bird life shift from time to time to the localities rendered most suitable by natural changes and by current land management.

Minsmere, on the estuarial clay at the mouth of the little Minsmere River, was first drained in 1813. From then until about 1940 the Level was mainly reclaimed grazing land intersected by the New Cut, which was improved by the newly-created Catchment Board during the nineteen-thirties. After war broke out the military authorities flooded the marshes with salt water and requisitioned them, while the adjoining heaths and woodlands were requisitioned for a battle training area. Woodlands, heaths and marshes were heavily bombarded, but the general effect of this rough treatment was to make Minsmere exceedingly attractive to birds, and in 1945 the Nature Reserves Investigation Committee said of it: 'Few, if any, comparable regions in England have such a rich and varied bird life.' In 1946 the owner, Captain A. S. Ogilvie, agreed to lease some 1,600 acres to the Royal Society for the Protection of Birds, who established the Nature Reserve almost simultaneously with the arrival in 1947 of four pairs of Avocets, which nested and reared at least eight young on one of the shallow lagoons, then still full of salt water. The following year, however, these birds apparently found Minsmere unsuitable and moved elsewhere; they have not bred here again.

As the wartime battleground was cleared of explosives and derequisitioned, Minsmere became once more a battleground between the conflicting forces of agricultural reclamation, afforestation, sport and nature conservation, with fires and renewed sea-flooding complicating the problem. Although some of the more southerly marshes were reclaimed, the Nature Reserve was successfully defended, and was effectively protected from disturbance by the R.S.P.B. warden and his voluntary helpers. On May 27, 1956, a fire lit by boys on Dunwich Common blew quickly through the adjoining reedbed into the northeast part of the Reserve called the Warren, but prompt and energetic efforts by local fire brigades, assisted by a large scratch force of firefighters, succeeded in confining damage to about 150 acres—a serious loss but small compared with earlier reports by Press and Radio giving the area destroyed as six square miles.

The Reserve includes a large acreage of reed-beds, some rough watermeadow, many shallow pools and dykes, some shingle and sand dunes, conifers and deciduous woodlands and much heath, some of it recently ploughed.

The birds of the Reserve are listed in the R.S.P.B.'s *Guide* (1s. 6d.), which accounts for 171 species noted during April-September in the four years 1948-51 alone. The *Guide* also contains a useful chart indicating the prospects of seeing different species in each of the months when Minsmere is most visited. The number of visitors given permits has to be strictly limited, 270 having been shown round in 1955.

Ninety species of birds, or half the number breeding regularly in the British Isles, bred on the Minsmere Reserve in 1955. Among these were

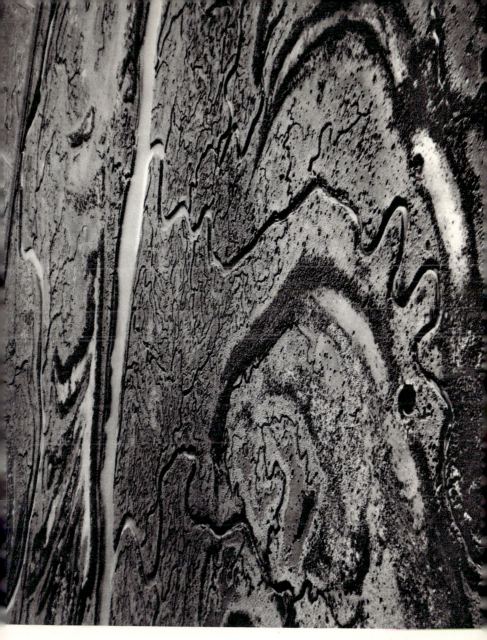

26. The saltmarsh on Scolt Head Island from the air. Winter feeding ground of Brent Geese.

27. Wicken Fen. An aerial photograph taken before the new Mere was excavated on Adventurer's Fen, centre right.

the Bittern (7-8 pairs), Garganey, Gadwall, Shoveler, Marsh Harrier, Stone Curlew, Woodlark, Bearded Tit (usually 12-20 pairs), Stonechat, Redstart, Grasshopper Warbler, Reed Warbler, Tree Pipit, Yellow Wagtail, Corn Bunting, Red-backed Shrike and Wheatear. The Little Ringed Plover and Montagu's Harrier have also bred in recent years. Spoonbills are regular visitors and such rarities as the White Stork and Crane have been seen.

The well-designed and well-sited wooden observation huts or 'hides' enable a surprisingly good sample of this rich bird life to be seen in considerable comfort and with a minimum of disturbance. One of these, on the sea-bank by the public coast path, is left open by the R.S.P.B. to all who pass, and from this vantage point it is possible to see Bitterns and Marsh Harriers without requiring a Reserve Permit. Within the Reserve the famous Tree Hide (plate No. 20) gives an excellent view over the marshes.

Orfordness-Havergate, Suffolk

NATURE CONSERVANCY RESERVE MANAGED AND PARTLY OWNED BY THE ROYAL SOCIETY FOR THE PROTECTION OF BIRDS

In East Suffolk, 1½ miles south of Orford: 514 acres. ACCESS. *Permits from R.S.P.B. required for whole Reserve except where otherwise marked by signs on part of Orfordness*

ALL ROUND the coast of England there is nothing stranger than the long shingle spit which stretches like a bent forefinger first southwards from Aldeburgh to Orfordness and then south-westwards to North Weir Point, with the River Alde or Ore on the west and the North Sea on the east. Erosion of the coast from northwards has created this great mass of shingle and by it has barred the natural outlet of the river to the sea at Aldeburgh and forced it to make the long additional journey past Orford until finally it escapes into the North Sea near Shingle Street. The point of this finger and the shingle and marshes opposite are of immense physiographical interest. They are among the most recent and most precarious additions to our Island and have much to tell us about the processes which build up new land and the way in which it becomes colonised with vegetation and with animal life.

Four miles of this shingle spit, stretching north-eastwards from its tip at North Weir Point, was declared a National Nature Reserve in 1954, together with the adjoining island of Havergate which had been bought by the Royal Society for the Protection of Birds in 1948. By a friendly understanding between the Society and the Conservancy, the Society warden the entire Reserve and provide transport, while the Nature Conservancy undertake research on problems other than ornithological and contribute to the heavy cost of protection against the sea.

The Reserve is very inaccessible for the ordinary holidaymaker and has few attractions. It is, therefore, a very suitable area to use for scientific and conservation work which requires complete absence of disturbance by the public.

While negotiations for the Reserve were still in progress the great North Sea surge of January 31, 1953, swept right over the shingle spit and the banks of Havergate Island, and actually floated one of the wooden observation huts from one to the other, from which it was eventually brought back and put into position again none the worse for its voyage.

The outstanding attraction of Havergate Island is the colony of Avocets which established itself there in 1947 when four pairs are thought to have reared eight young. In 1948 six pairs settled but only three young were reared, largely because of rats. In 1956, 79 pairs reared at least 50 young. This growth of the colony is very remarkable when it is borne in mind that the Avocet needs peculiar saline conditions with plenty of shallow water over a muddy bottom in order to obtain its food. Probably the most extensive favourable area for Avocets in Europe is the Camargue, and yet it is now estimated that not more than about 200 pairs of Avocets breed there, which is only about three times the population of Havergate. This must mean that the Royal Society for the Protection of Birds has been as successful in providing the right feeding conditions as in protecting the birds from collectors, rodents and other pests. Neither success would have availed without the other.

The Avocets apparently benefited in their initial colonisation from the presence of a large number of breeding Black-headed Gulls which helped to give protection against Crows and other predators. They in turn have helped to provide the conditions to attract a colony of Sandwich Terns, the first to be formed so far as is known in Suffolk. About 30 pairs of them bred on the Island in 1951, and by 1954 the colony had increased to about 150 pairs. This is the only Sandwich Tern colony in England which is not directly facing the sea. Almost certainly the ex-

28. *Woodwalton Fen Nature Reserve from the air showing extent of scrub colonisation due to long interruption in maintenance of high water level before 1954.*

29. Large Copper Butterfly found in upper section of Woodwalton Fen (Plate 28).

30. Holme Fen Nature Reserve with pillar top marking ground level in 1851.

ceptional protection at Havergate has induced them to accept a breeding site which they would otherwise reject as unsuitable. About 100 pairs of Common Terns breed on Havergate and a similar number have bred at North Weir Point where 129 nests with eggs were found in 1953.

A grant from the Nature Conservancy has made it financially possible for the Royal Society for the Protection of Birds to discontinue letting the shooting in winter, and this in turn has enabled the sheltered waters of Havergate to become a complete year-round sanctuary for ducks and other wildfowl. The total number of species of birds recorded within the Reserve now stands at 154.

Havergate is also of interest as being the type locality, and only haunt, of a new spider named *Praestigia duffeyi* after its discoverer, the Regional Officer for East Anglia of the Nature Conservancy. These semi-marine spiders live on the saltings close to the observation post maintained to enable bird watchers to study the Avocets without disturbing them. The provision of such observation posts, which are quite cheaply constructed and are built to a special design is one of the most important recent developments in Nature Reserve management. It is the key to the problem of enabling considerable numbers of visitors to see shy birds without creating so much disturbance as to drive them away. The sea-banks serve the important secondary purpose of enabling observers to gain access to the observation posts without showing themselves to the birds.

Orfordness is also of great interest as illustrating the stages in plant colonisation from bare, loose shingle with a few pioneer plants, to consolidated areas covered with vegetation.

The R.S.P.B. has produced a guide to the birds of Havergate (1s. 6d.), similar to that on Minsmere.

Hickling Broad, Norfolk

NORFOLK NATURALISTS TRUST RESERVE

12 miles north-east of Norwich: 600 acres. ACCESS. *Restricted, except on waterways*

WITH their wide horizons and bright skies and their wealth of vegetation and animal life, the Norfolk Broads form a link with the marshland across the North Sea, especially in the Netherlands. Although none of the Broads is of very great size, a number of them are

G

of outstanding interest to the naturalist and they show a remarkable variety of conditions. If one must be chosen as an example of all, Hickling naturally has the first claim.

Hickling is very little above sea level and is only three miles from the North Sea, which has broken into it twice during the past 20 years; on February 12, 1938, and on January 31, 1953. The age-long contest between land and sea for the possession of this area is, therefore, still in progress, and a comparatively slight shift in their relative levels could be very inconvenient to the coast defences. At the same time the problem of maintaining sufficient open water against the advance of aquatic vegetation is also serious. Another of the management problems of the Reserve is to preserve the right proportion between reed beds, open flooded grasslands and woody carrs.

Up to the beginning of this century, the Broads were helped to keep open by the traffic of wherries and by the regular mowing of the marshes for litter, and as food for (among other consumers) the horses which used to draw the London buses. Economic changes have much reduced the demand for the marsh vegetation, although there is still a good market for first-class Norfolk reed for thatching the roofs of houses.

During the past ten years, however, Hickling and other Broads have been invaded by large numbers of Coypus (*Myocastor coypus*). These large South American rodents may measure over two feet long without their tails and weigh about 10-20 pounds. They rear on an average around five young in about two litters a year, and they feed on aquatic plants in such quantities that they are capable of eliminating all vegetation emerging from the water over several acres. While opinions are divided, there seems so far to be no evidence that the Coypu is anything but beneficial, and while there has been considerable discussion about increasing the area of open water for navigation in the Broads, the Coypu can claim to have been so far the only creature to do anything effective about it.

Hickling is most famous for its rare breeding birds, and particularly the Marsh (and sometimes Montagu's) Harriers, the Bearded Tit and the Bittern, and for such visitors as the Ruff and Reeve, the Spoonbill and the Osprey. The birds were protected for many years by the late Lord Desborough, who was succeeded by the Norfolk Naturalists Trust. The problems of public control are considerable, owing to the large number of visitors who sail or pass in motor-cruisers through the Broad, but the dense reed beds and swampy ground discourage the vast majority from seeking to penetrate far beyond the main channels. A more serious problem is the control of the vegetation so as to keep in check ecological changes harmful to the wild life.

A record of observations, especially of the birds at Hickling, has been kept up over many years, notably by the late Jim Vincent and the late Miss E. L. Turner. The effects of the 1938 incursion of the sea on vegetation and animal life have also been very fully recorded in the transactions of the Norfolk and Norwich Naturalists' Society, while more recently experiments in various types of vegetation control have been undertaken with the aid of the Nature Conservancy.

Weeting Heath, Norfolk

NORFOLK NATURALISTS TRUST RESERVE

On the Norfolk bank of the Little Ouse River, just west of Brandon:
350 acres. ACCESS. *Restricted*

UP TO 40 years ago the Breckland district of Norfolk and Suffolk kept very much its ancient character as one of the finest and least disturbed of England's wide open spaces. Although the chalk so closely underlies it, this is a very different type of chalk country from the downs of southern England. It is comparatively flat and low-lying, being less than 50 feet above sea level. Some nineteenth-century planting of Scots Pine had interrupted the more distant views, but the peculiar hedges and wind-breaks of Pines had a special charm and fitness in the scene, and they brought with them an enrichment of the wild life. Since 1914 unfortunately most of this beauty and natural heritage has been ruthlessly obliterated. Airfields, bombing targets, battle-training areas, ranges and an enormous acreage of planted conifers have invaded the old Breckland, leaving only a handful of remnants of what it was like even within living memory.

One of the best of these remnants is Weeting Heath on the Norfolk bank of the Little Ouse River, just west of Brandon, extending in a long finger northwards from the river to the main road from Brandon to King's Lynn. The northern part of Weeting Heath is a typical grass heath floristically rich and on a deep calcareous soil of the type which, under rabbit grazing, produces masses of attractive wild flowers such as Thyme, Milkwort, Squinancywort and Purging Flax, including some considerable rarities. All these require grazing for their successful survival and in its absence they become dominated by grasses. The southern part of the heath has a deeper soil and this type requires to be lightly ploughed from time to time in order to maintain its character. Grasses grow on it better than herbs.

Weeting Heath was acquired by the foresight of the Norfolk Naturalists Trust and one of the main objects of the Reserve is to provide a permanent refuge for the characteristic open-loving Breckland birds such as the Stone Curlew, Wheatear, Woodlark and Nightjar, which are so rapidly losing the greater part of their former habitat.

Among the invertebrates of the heath are two very scarce spiders.

Scolt Head, Norfolk

NATURE CONSERVANCY RESERVE

3 miles north of Burnham Market on the coast: 1,821 *acres.*
Leased from the National Trust and the Norfolk Naturalists Trust.
ACCESS. *Unrestricted*

SCOLT HEAD Island, on the north coast of Norfolk, is one of the oldest Nature Reserves in England, having been acquired for the National Trust in 1923. It is also one of the Reserves which have been most thoroughly studied by scientists, particularly from Cambridge University. Investigations have been made of the growth of the dunes, of the movement of beach material, of the evolution of the salt marshes and of the vegetation, invertebrates, mammals and birds.

The Island is owned mainly by the National Trust, but partly by the Norfolk Naturalists Trust, and the two Trusts have leased it (together with Dial House on the mainland at Brancaster Staithe) to the Nature Conservancy, which is responsible for the management. All important questions are referred to the Committee which represents the two Trusts as well as the Conservancy and the local inhabitants. There is a full-time Warden, Mr Robert Chestney, who lives at the Dial House, Brancaster Staithe, where there is also limited accommodation for naturalists, some of whom also live in the hut on the Island while doing field work there.

The Reserve is about four miles long and consists of a series of dune ridges, in places very well developed, over-lying shingle; between the dunes and the mainland lie extensive salt marshes, which are completely submerged at high tide. The shape and size of the Island are continually changing and during this century there has been a considerable extension to the west.

It is on this westward point that the main colony of breeding seabirds is located. Just before the Island became a Nature Reserve there were no Sandwich Terns breeding and Common Terns were reduced to some 17 pairs. Under protection, the numbers rose rapidly and in addition to a much stronger colony of Common Terns, which has at times reached about 1,000 breeding pairs, Sandwich Terns have also bred in considerable numbers in many years. In 1956, 900 nests of Common Terns and 74 of Sandwich Terns were marked. Little Terns also breed regularly in considerable numbers. In winter the Island is frequented by a large number of immigrant species, including Snow Buntings and Shore Larks.

Ecologically the Island is of immense interest owing to the exceptionally favourable conditions for tracing the different zones and the successive colonisations of different plant communities. It is also the home of a large number of plants of the dunes, shingle and salt marshes, and the flowering of some of these was spectacularly assisted by the disappearance of the large rabbit population following myxomatosis in 1955.

Recent experiments have been made with radio-active elements inserted into pebbles, the object being to trace the rate and direction of drift of the pebbles under the sea by the use of a boat carrying a Geiger Counter, and thus to help to interpret the coast-shaping forces. The great North Sea surge of January 31, 1953, came completely over the middle of the Island and resulted in a large breach which has been filled in by the planting of Marram Grass and by suitable coast defence works.

It is hoped that with the growing interest in nature, visitors will increasingly learn to behave in ways which will not damage the wild life for which Scolt Head is one of the most important refuges in East Anglia.

Wicken Fen, Cambridgeshire

NATIONAL TRUST RESERVE

Some 6 miles south of Ely: 730 acres. ACCESS. *See p. 77*

'FEN', IN the restricted use of the term by biologists, is a type of vegetation dominated by grasses, rushes or sedges, and developed on peat saturated with fresh water. It is typically a stage in the development of 'dry land' vegetation which begins when open water becomes choked with water-plants and reed swamp, and ends with some kind of woodland. Not infrequently fens are actually flanked by open water or waterways and by spurs of higher and drier ground or of ground which has gradually been drained by the transformation to woodland.

In England the great flat area almost at sea level stretching from the Wash to Peterborough and Cambridge is often called the Fenland. Although successive drainage and reclamation schemes have reduced that fragment which can truly be called fen to an insignificant proportion of its present extent, these few surviving areas are of irreplaceable scientific value and probably the most important of them is Wicken Fen, on the right bank of the River Cam, some six miles south of the great Cathedral of Ely, which dominates the Fenland.

This square mile of land was acquired in many instalments between 1899 and recent years by the National Trust for Places of Historic Interest and Natural Beauty. Being of special interest to Cambridge University biologists, it was placed under a local Committee on which the University scientists have played the leading part. The fen has accordingly been the scene of a great deal of scientific research, some of the earlier results of which were published in six parts containing 56 separate contributions between 1923 and 1932 under the editorship of Professor J. Stanley Gardner, F.R.S., who was then Secretary of the Committee.

The scientists recognised from the early stages that the sentimental idea of leaving the fen to nature was not a practical management policy and would merely result in the interesting rarities being suppressed by a few dominant species. The character of the fen for centuries had been due to its management for the sake of the once valuable sedge crop and the Trust had to ensure that excessive growth is thinned, waterways properly kept, and suitable conditions maintained for the characteristic fenland species. The Committee also had in mind to enrich the habitat by re-creating a mere such as once covered the site. After heavy wartime setbacks, when Adventurer's Fen was partially reclaimed for agriculture, this ambition was finally realised in 1955.

Wicken Sedge Fen represents a relic of the original uncultivated fenland and its level is slightly above that of the adjoining waterways, while Adventurer's Fen is some five or six feet lower and is hardly above sea level at some points. This makes the water supply to the mere an easy matter, especially as it rests on the underlying boulder clay. Trunks of many great oaks were excavated during the wartime reclamation here in 1941, having been preserved in extremely good condition for some 5,000 years beneath the covering of peat.

The Alder Buckthorn (*Frangula alnus*) is probably more abundant on Wicken Sedge Fen than anywhere else in Britain—indeed, its control is the greatest problem of management which the Committee has to face—and during the last war, when supplies from abroad were cut off, its wood was used for making charcoal for time fuses, for which its uniform and even-burning qualities were vital. This is an example of an obscure species proving of economic importance.

While part of the fen is kept quiet for the benefit of shy birds and other animals, visitors are permitted freely to explore the pathways along the banks of the Lodes, as the larger waterways are called, and also those bordering the smaller drains, after signing their names in the visitors' book at the Keeper's house.

Ornithologically, Wicken Fen is most celebrated as one of the main strongholds of Savi's Warbler until its disappearance in 1856. A male came back and sang its strange reeling song on the fen through most of the summer of 1954, when it was heard and seen with great pleasure by many naturalists. The excellent guide published by the National Trust indicates that the fen must contain at least 5,000 species of insects, including 1,075 kinds of beetles and 757 of butterflies and moths which have actually been authenticated. Many of these species are either known only from Wicken or are exceedingly rare elsewhere. Altogether, 183 species of spiders have been recorded, six of which are peculiar to the fen, and 13 species of earthworms, one of which is a peculiar form. More than 300 species of flowering plants have been recorded on the National Trust property. While a small number of these, such as the Fen Violet (*Viola stagnina*), has become extinct at Wicken since their first record in the last century, there are many local fen species still abundant. Perhaps the best-known are the Milk-parsley (*Peucedanum palustre*), the Marsh Pea (*Lathyrus palustris*), and the Bladderwort (*Utricularia vulgaris*).

Woodwalton Fen, Huntingdonshire

NATURE CONSERVANCY RESERVE

10 *miles south-east of Peterborough:* 514 *acres. Leased from the Society for the Promotion of Nature Reserves.* ACCESS. *Permits to visit required for whole Reserve*

DURING the wholesale destruction of the old fen habitats caused by drainage and reclamation, a small out-of-the-way area some three miles west of Ramsey in Huntingdonshire escaped total ruin, partly because it was at intervals dug for turf or peat as fuel, partly because the rough litter growing on it was cut as hay or was grazed by livestock, and partly because such agriculture as was practised amounted literally to no more than scratching the surface. Early this century the old fenland management on these lines ceased to function and tall reeds spread extensively. In turn the reed was succeeded by dense carr, chiefly of sallow willows, and eventually by scrub woodland which threatened to transform the whole fen into an uninteresting damp forest.

Through the generosity of the Hon. Charles Rothschild, the Society for the Promotion of Nature Reserves was enabled from 1919 onwards to acquire in instalments more than 500 acres of the fen, forming a broad rectangle immediately to the west of the Great Raveley Drain. Although some 25 miles from the sea, this fen is nowhere more than about two feet above sea-level and the drastic drainage and pumping necessary to protect the adjoining farmlands makes it increasingly difficult to maintain a high enough water-table for the requirements of the aquatic and fenland fauna and flora. The tendency of the fen to dry out is mainly responsible for its invasion by woody vegetation.

The Society struggled for many years against these adverse influences, which were greatly aggravated by the Second World War and by the great increase in labour costs resulting from the subsequent inflation. Eventually in 1954 the Society leased the Reserve to the Nature Conservancy, while retaining a close interest in it through the medium of a local committee. After a detailed botanical survey, the Conservancy set in hand extensive works to raise and maintain the water level and to check and reverse the encroachment of fen by woodland and scrub vegetation. Dykes were cleaned out, sluices were installed and peat cut-

31. Holme Fen Nature Reserve. Aerial view and map showing part of bed of Whittlesey Mere, drained in 1851.

32. Monks' Wood Nature Reserve. Aerial view showing copious but poor natural regeneration since clear felling forty years ago.

ting was resumed to permit scientific observation on the process of recolonisation by plants.

Aquatic plants flourished and a rare hybrid pondweed (*Potamogeton fluitans*) was re-discovered after being considered extinct for many years; while in July, 1955, a Dutch member of the International Ecological Commission, during a short visit to the fen, detected *Myriophyllum alterniflorum*, which has not been recorded in Huntingdonshire since about 1830. Heavy floods in December, 1954, enabled the fen to re-absorb a great deal of moisture to the benefit of the neighbouring farmlands, which were relieved of large quantities of flood water. Shortly afterwards, myxomatosis among rabbits set in train further extensive ecological changes and enabled many previously rare plants to flower as never before.

Woodwalton is famous for its insects and particularly for the Large Copper Butterfly, one of the most beautiful insects we have. The original British race became extinct following the drainage of Whittlesey Mere a century ago. The present stock which belongs to the Netherlands race, *Lycaena dispar batavus*, was introduced in 1927. Efforts to introduce it to other areas have hitherto failed, but the Large Coppers at Woodwalton can be seen on the wing in some numbers in July of each year. Many very rare moths and other insects have been taken in the fen, which is a well-known resort of collectors, although access requires an official permit. The more characteristic marsh birds, such as the Short-eared Owl, which used formerly to breed, have ceased in recent years, but it is hoped that they can be attracted again with the increasing open area resulting from scrub clearance.

Although called a fen, Woodwalton differs considerably from Wicken and was probably a Sphagnum bog with local areas of fen flushes up to the time of the general fenland drainage. Cutting has in many places removed the Sphagnum peat and exposed the alkaline fen peat of an earlier period underlying it. This has produced interesting differences in the flora and the fauna.

The experience of Woodwalton shows that even when apparently irreparable deterioration has occurred, it is some times possible to resurrect the previous conditions, given the right type of management.

H

Holme Fen, Huntingdonshire

NATURE CONSERVANCY RESERVE

6 miles south of Peterborough: 640 acres. ACCESS. *Permits required for the whole Reserve*

UNTIL just over a hundred years ago, the largest sheet of water in Southern England was Whittlesey Mere, about five miles south of Peterborough. Immediately south-west of this mere and adjoining the present main line from King's Cross to Edinburgh lay the marshy ground which now forms the square-mile Nature Reserve of Holme Fen. In 1851 Whittlesey Mere was drained with the aid of a type of steam pump which had been exhibited that year in the Great Exhibition at the Crystal Palace. As the Mere emptied, enormous numbers of Pike, Perch, Bream, Roach and Chub were caught or left to rot, and as the mud dried a great catch of eels was made.

When the Great Exhibition was dismantled towards the end of 1851, one of the iron columns from the old Crystal Palace was driven 22 feet through the peat until its top was level with the ground surface. Within ten years the ground level had fallen through shrinkage by nearly five feet, and within 40 years it was ten feet below the top of the pillar. The original ground level is now six feet above the head of a six-foot man walking about in the Reserve. This would seem almost incredible if a careful record had not been kept. Immediately after the drainage the area was reclaimed for agriculture, and this continued until the late nineteenth century when the excessive shrinkage caused it to be abandoned. It then became a sporting estate with planted coverts of Birch, Pine and other trees. Bracken also was deliberately introduced.

During the Second World War the Ministry of Supply used the area for charcoal production for explosives, and extensive felling took place. Drainage was also intensified. Although all these changes were unfortunate for wild life, a number of interesting plants and animals managed to survive and in 1952 the wheel turned full circle with the declaration of the Nature Reserve designed to enable the old fenland fauna and flora to recover so far as they could. The havoc of a century may take the better part of a further century to repair, particularly since the deepening of drains and consequent lowering of the water table is continuing.

The greater part of the area remains under woodland, and the Nature

Conservancy's researches include studies of the growth of the Birch, which for some unknown reason hardly ever grows so satisfactorily in England as in the Baltic countries. The Holme Fen Duck Decoy constructed in 1815 is stated to have taken up to 30 dozen birds daily in its early days. Its present value is mainly as a last refuge of some of the fen plants which have managed to survive there. The breeding birds include Woodcock, Willow Tits and a number of species of Warblers, as well as many Nightingales. Part of the Reserve can be seen on the east of the main line to Edinburgh as the train runs along the embankment immediately north of Holme village and station. Great difficulties were met in constructing this railway over the unstable peat, and even now some peculiar effects are noticed in very dry summers.

Monks' Wood, Huntingdonshire

NATURE CONSERVANCY RESERVE

Some 5 miles north-east of Huntingdon: 387 acres. ACCESS. *Permits required for the whole Reserve*

A FEW centuries ago the raised plateau of heavy clays bordering the Huntingdonshire fenlands carried a great forest of Ash and Oak rich in many forms of wild life. The monks of Sawtry Abbey (which lay about three miles north of the Alconbury Hill Junction on the Great North Road and about half a mile west of the main railway line from Edinburgh to King's Cross) acquired a part of this forest and apparently saved it from being cleared away as most of the rest was. The largest surviving fragment is now the Monks' Wood Nature Reserve.

Early in the nineteenth century the wood became famous among entomologists through the discovery there in 1828, for the first time in Britain, of the Black Hairstreak Butterfly (*Strymonidia pruni*). All four other species of British Hairstreak and many other interesting butterflies, including the Purple Emperor, continued to attract entomologists until the 1914-18 war, when as many as 20 male Purple Emperors could be seen on the wing. The wood was at that time maintained in perfect condition by its owner, Lord Chesham, on a 20-year rotation. Disaster overtook it about 1920 when wholesale felling of the timber was carried out by Canadian lumbermen so drastically that more than half of the wood became a desert of grey ashes.

The trees showed considerable powers of recovery, but the scrub woodland and thickets which replaced the original tall Oak forest had nothing like its botanical or zoological value. It was, however, lovingly preserved by an entomologist, Mr H. Neaverson, until the Nature Conservancy acquired it in 1953, by which time the Second World War had left further scars in the shape of two large clearings designed for potato fields. These were not successful and are being allowed to revert to nature.

Although the Purple Emperors seem to have become extinct, and also the Duke of Burgundy Fritillaries, the wood still has a remarkable range of butterflies and of moths, including all the Hairstreaks, the White Admiral and the Comma Butterfly, which first appeared about 1935.

The management of the Nature Reserve is designed to secure the eventual re-establishment of tall forest to maintain the best possible conditions for the survival of the utmost variety of insect life. Ornithologically and botanically the wood, although interesting, contains nothing out of the ordinary.

Skokholm, Pembrokeshire

WEST WALES FIELD SOCIETY
AND FIELD STUDIES COUNCIL RESERVE

West of the entrance to Milford Haven, 3 miles south of Skomer: 240 acres. Held under lease. ACCESS. *Restricted*

COMMANDING the northern entrance to the Bristol Channel lie the three famous Pembrokeshire bird islands—Grassholm, Skomer and Skokholm. While Grassholm is no more than a rock, Skokholm is a 240 acre plateau more than a mile long and rising to 175 feet above the sea, flanked by cliffs of Old Red Sandstone, against which waves break in south-westerly gales with all the force which their fetch of over 4,000 miles confers on them.

The history of Skokholm is extremely well documented since the early Middle Ages, when, with Skomer, it was one of the earliest and most important rabbit warrens after the introduction of rabbits to Britain. More than 3,000 rabbits are recorded as having been taken in the winter of 1387-8 from the islands of Skokholm and Skomer. After being successfully farmed the island became uninhabited in late

33. *Gannets on Grassholm.*

34. *Grassholm from the air, showing Gannets along ridge.*

35. *Royal Fern (Osmunda regalis).*

36. Cader Idris Nature Reserve. View west along Cader Idris escarpment from Mynydd Moel toward Penygadair.

37. *Cwm Idwal Nature Reserve from the air with Llyn Idwal in foreground.*

38. *Lloydia serotina growing in the Cwm Idwal Reserve.*

Victorian times. The lighthouse was built in 1914. In 1927 Mr R. M. Lockley took a lease and farmed it with sheep, but he was eventually defeated by the great and increasing rabbit population after deciding to abandon the use of steel traps on account of the danger to wild birds.

In 1929 Lockley began work on his classic study of the habits of the Manx Shearwater which led to this species becoming the best understood species of Petrel in the world. Lockley's experiments with ringed Shearwaters showed the immense distances from which they were able to find their way back to Skokholm and their almost incredible habit of going to fetch food from as far away as the southern end of the Bay of Biscay. In 1933 Lockley started on Skokholm the earliest bird observatory in Great Britain and ringed in that season 175 birds.

Among other pioneer scientific work done on Skokholm at this period were the first field trials of myxomatosis as a method of controlling rabbit populations and the nearly successful extermination of rabbits by the use of cyanide gas on a large scale. Following the evacuation of the sheep in 1934, six Soay sheep were obtained from Woburn and a flock of some 50 now lives in a wild state on the island. After being evacuated on account of the war in 1940, the bird observatory was again operated from 1946 by the West Wales Field Society (which holds the lease); and from 1948 by the Field Studies Council by arrangement with the W.W.F.S.

During 1955 some 200 visitors from as far afield as Australia, South Africa, Norway, Germany and Holland took part in the work on the island between March and October. They recorded 123 species of birds and ringed 7,168 belonging to 66 different species. Some extremely rare birds occur on migration at Skokholm almost every year. Investigations have been made into a number of other groups, including ectoparasites and marine invertebrates. Dr Mary E. Gillham has made a detailed study of the vegetation, including such aspects as the effects of salt spray and the extensions of Ragwort and of Bracken. The large colonies of Puffins and of Storm Petrels and Wheatears have also been investigated in detail.

In the winter the Warden withdraws to Dale Fort, which is nearby on the mainland at the entrance to Milford Haven—it acts as 'parent' to the Observatory, being also one of the Field Centres of the Field Studies Council.

Grassholm, Pembrokeshire

ROYAL SOCIETY FOR THE PROTECTION OF BIRDS AND WEST WALES FIELD SOCIETY RESERVE

About 14 miles south-west of St David's, and about 7 miles west of Skomer: 23 acres. ACCESS. *Restricted*

GRASSHOLM is a little island in the eastern entry to St. George's Channel. It is a low rock of basalt covering only 22 acres and is ecologically interesting, not only for its remoteness, but because it has never been permanently inhabited nor, so far as is known, grazed either by domestic or wild mammals. Wind exposure, salt spray and the lack of soil restrict the plant life to a very few species; only 12 flowering plants being of any importance. Fescue Grass (*Festuca rubra*) dominates the vegetation. Over many centuries it has formed a soil rich in organic matter which is so soft that a man sinks into it at every stride.

The history of Grassholm is little known, but it appears that there were a very few breeding pairs of Gannets, at least during the early nineteenth century, and only during the First World War did the population rise to about a thousand pairs. After that it doubled by 1924 and rose to about 4,750 pairs in 1933, about 6,000 in 1940 and about 9,000 in 1949. In 1956 R. M. Lockley noticed the outline of a stone-walled bird-catching corral, possibly several hundred years old, on the edge of the Gannet colony, indicating that the Gannets may once have been as numerous as they are to-day.

Puffins colonised probably a century or two ago at least, but it was only in the late nineteenth century that the colony was known to be very large (estimated at about quarter of a million pairs in 1890, or two to three for every square yard). Their burrows completely undermine the vegetation and by 1928 the great majority had left. In 1948 the population of Puffins was estimated at only 75 pairs, the remaining species on the island being 100 pairs of Herring Gulls, 60 of Great Black-backed Gulls, 120 of Kittiwakes, 150 of Guillemots, 40 of Razorbills, 4 of Oystercatchers, 5 of Rock Pipits, 2 of Shags and 1 of Ravens. These, mixed together with about 9,000 pairs of Gannets, made a substantial population for 22 acres.

According to a letter quoted by R. M. Lockley (from whose accounts this information is derived), there was a small colony of Roseate Terns there in 1885 and shortly after that a pair of Peregrines bred.

The island was bought in 1947 by the Royal Society for the Protection of Birds, who arranged with the West Wales Field Society to act as local custodians. This step was very welcome as, apart from raids by unauthorised visitors, the island had suffered during the latter part of the war from being used as a bombing target.

Cors Tregaron, Cardiganshire

NATURE CONSERVANCY RESERVE

12 *miles south-east of Aberystwyth:* 1,524 *acres. Under Nature Reserve Agreement with the Earl of Lisburne.* ACCESS. *Permits required for whole Reserve*

PEAT bogs are the most difficult of all types of Nature Reserves for ordinary people to appreciate. As scenery they look dreary, as land-use wasteful, and as open spaces perilous and unrewarding to walk over. Yet the arguments for preserving before it is too late an adequate series of British peat bogs are very strong. Our rainy, windy, oceanic climate has given us in the British Isles a remarkably high proportion of the world's best-developed peat bogs, and there is nowhere else in Europe, apart from Ireland, where any neglect by us to preserve examples for posterity could be redressed.

For generations lowland raised bogs have been a main target for land reclaimers and many of the best examples have been drained, while others have been so exploited and burnt over that their scientific value has been ruined. Yet a large raised bog is one of the most remarkable works of nature in Britain, extending sometimes over several miles and having built up a mass of vegetation as much as twenty or more feet above the surrounding country, so waterlogged as sometimes to appear in conflict with the law that water runs downhill. The enormous water-holding capacity of these bogs is a safeguard against flooding of the adjoining and down-river land. They can also, like Cors Tregaron, serve as giant natural filters, taking in polluted water at one end and discharging it absolutely pure at the other.

Peat bogs moreover form natural refuges and reservoirs for scarce plants and animals which have been exterminated in other habitats. Without them our fauna and flora would be much the poorer. Economically they are our only renewable resources of solid fuel. Peat has the property of preserving undecayed for many centuries anything embedded in it, such as pollen, roots, tree trunks, or even human bodies. It is therefore of special importance in understanding the past.

In England and Wales studies of raised bogs have recently been concentrated on the site of a former lake in the Teifi Valley above Tregaron in central Wales, which in Post-Glacial times became filled by fen peat over which have developed three large raised bogs. Between these the Teifi flows in snake-like meanderings, with the largest bog on its right bank and the other two on its left. This area, about 540 feet above sea-level, was investigated during 1936-7 by a large party of botanists from Cambridge, Oxford, Newcastle, Cardiff, Dublin and Aberystwyth, and being defeated by the Welsh name Cors-Goch-Glan-Teifi, the English botanists called it Tregaron Bog. In 1955 it was declared a National Nature Reserve under agreement between the Nature Conservancy and the owner, Lord Lisburne, whose family have for long cared for it and protected it. As a compromise between the Welsh and the English, the title Cors Tregaron was adopted.

The remarkable character of this Nature Reserve can best be seen from air photographs. One of the interesting botanical discoveries was that the great bulk of the bog is formed of a species of bog-moss (*Sphagnum imbricatum*), which has now become extinct over the whole area, for reasons which are still not fully understood. Several other species of Sphagnum are, however, still actively at work in their specialised functions, *Sphagnum cuspidatum* lining the open water pools and *S. papillosum* creating the characteristic hummocks of the uneven bog surface. It appears that the bog is growing only slowly at the present day, as it did during dry periods in the past, and in contrast to its active growth in the cold wet climate of Iron Age Britain.

The present rainfall is about 50 inches annually. Like all typical raised bogs, those at Tregaron are dome-shaped, rising in the centre as much as 25 feet above the river level. On the north-west side the 'lagg' vegetation is best developed, where the edge of the domed surface of the bog meets water draining from the surrounding countryside, yielding a greater mineral content in the soil and supporting richer vegetation, with dense growth of grasses and sedges and low trees of Willow and Birch and some Rowan and Hawthorn, visible in the aerial view. Compared with most large bogs Tregaron has suffered relatively little from fire or from peat-cutting, except near the edges, or from drainage schemes. It is, therefore, a magnificent outdoor laboratory for further research—for example, on past climatic changes, which have already

39. *Newborough Warren Nature Reserve. Aerial view with Ynys Llanddwyn.*

40. *Newborough Dunes looking south. Re-invigorated Marram on secondary mobile sand in foreground (centre). The low-lying flat region, centre left, is a dry slack colonised by Salix repens. Semi-fixed Marram dunes lie beyond the slack. The mountains of Snowdonia are in the background.*

41. *Gibraltar Point and Skegness Reserves. Aerial view showing dunes and slacks down to Bird Observatory on dunes near lower left corner.*

been partly revealed by pollen analysis. Its closeness to Aberystwyth is an additional advantage fully appreciated by the University of Wales.

Among the interesting plants of Tregaron are the beautiful Marsh Andromeda (*Andromeda polifolia*), the Crowberry (*Empetrum nigrum*), normally found at much higher altitudes, and the Royal Fern (*Osmunda regalis*), which has been eliminated by collectors and gardeners from most of its more accessible haunts.

The breeding birds include the Blackcock, Dunlin, Corncrake, Whinchat, Grasshopper Warbler, Redpoll and two colonies of Black-headed Gulls. The most interesting ornithological feature, however, is the use of the bog by a flock of up to 500 of the recently distinguished race of Greenland White-fronted Geese, which have here their only regular important wintering area in England and Wales. The breeding haunts of these birds are now protected in Greenland and it is agreeable to be able to reciprocate that service to us by assuring the Geese of adequate protection during their stay here. Polecats, which are fortunately not uncommon in the neighbourhood, are perhaps the most interesting of the local mammals.

Cader Idris, Merionethshire

NATURE CONSERVANCY RESERVE

About 4 miles south-west of Dolgelly: 969 acres. ACCESS. *Unrestricted*

CADER IDRIS means Arthur's Seat and its great importance to geologists and botanists is matched by its place in legend and as scenery. Geologically, Cader Idris is a classic site for the study of Ordovician rocks, sedimentary and volcanic, including lavas and shales, with a band of iron ore. The interest is enhanced by the long past volcanic activity which took place partly under the sea.

After being raised to a far greater altitude than at present, the mountain was subjected to forces which shaped it towards its present form long before the Ice Ages, although glacial action completed the process, particularly by hollowing out the almost perfect corrie-lakes, such as Llyn Cau. Geologists have pointed out close parallels in Antarctica to the scenery of this region. The mountains are, therefore, as interesting to physiographers, tracing how they received their present shape, as to

I

geologists tracing the age and composition of the rocks from which they are made.

The differing mineral nutrients contained in these rocks, both basic and acid, and their differing arrangements of ledges, crags, drainage and soils, slopes and exposures, rainfalls (ranging up to 100 inches or more) and altitudes give rise to a wide variety of habitat and of plant communities. Cader Idris is one of the most southern outposts in Britain of the Arctic-Alpine flora characteristic of the higher mountains of Snowdonia, including such species as the Welsh Poppy, the Mossy Saxifrage (*Saxifraga hypnoides*), Starry Saxifrage (*Saxifraga stellaris*), the Mountain Sorrel, Roseroot and, among rarities, a lichen (*Pertusaria monogona*) and the Hairy Greenweed (*Genista pilosa*), first recorded here in 1800, but afterwards lost sight of for nearly a century until it was rediscovered in quantity on the mountain.

Sir Arthur Tansley in *The British Islands and their Vegetation* chose Cader Idris to contrast with Ben Lawers, probably the richest example of Arctic-Alpine flora in Great Britain; considering its much more southerly position and lower altitude (2,927 feet against 3,984), Cader Idris does not compare unfavourably, especially where variety of habitats is involved.

Cader Idris has been the subject of important botanical studies, notably by Price Evans, which have shown that in former times trees grew about 650 feet higher than nowadays when the treeline is at about 1,100 feet. The mountain top is dominated largely by the Woolly Fringed Moss (*Rhacomitrium lanuginosum*). Some of the thousand-foot precipices have a characteristic limited flora and the extensive screes and moraines present interesting problems for research, although scientists working in these conditions require to be exceptionally fit and sure-footed. Although so well known, the mountain is not visited by such large numbers of walkers and climbers as some of those in Snowdonia.

Cader Idris became a Nature Reserve through the public-spirited action of the owners, Idris Limited, who concluded in respect of it the first Nature Reserve Agreement in Wales.

Cwm Idwal, Caernarvonshire

NATURE CONSERVANCY RESERVE

6 *miles west of Capel Curig:* 984 *acres. Leased from the National Trust.* ACCESS. *Unrestricted*

SNOWDONIA, with its great variety of rocks, altitudes, exposures, rainfall and consequently vegetation and animal life, is a region of special interest for ecological research and nature conservation, but it is also within one of the most popular National Parks of Britain and the remoteness and lack of disturbance which for so long assured the survival of its fauna and flora are a thing of the past. The Nature Conservancy, in an effort to reconcile these conflicting interests, established the first National Nature Reserve in Wales, and the first Nature Reserve within a National Park at Cwm Idwal in 1954. The Reserve begins above Ogwen Cottage, slightly above the thousand-foot contour, and includes the waters of Llyn Idwal and three others, the highest lying at 2,300 feet. The highest point of the Reserve on Glyder Fawr is 3,279 feet, which is considerably higher than Cader Idris. The summit is dominated by Woolly Fringed Moss (*R. lanuginosum*) and a large part of the area is within the Arctic-Alpine zone of vegetation, the remainder being chiefly mountain grassland with a little heather moor.

Recent research by the method of pollen analysis shows that after the melting of the glacier which occupied the cwm in the last Ice Age, characteristic mountain plants established themselves and were here able to maintain themselves through the Post-Glacial period when in most other areas they were displaced by the competition either of woodland or of peat bog vegetation. It seems certain that several of the most characteristic plants have been there ever since the Ice Age, including *Armeria maritima* and *Plantago maritima*, which are now normally found on the sea coast, and in scattered localities on high mountain tops. The Crowberry (*Empetrum*) is another example of a plant which grew about Llyn Idwal in the late Glacial period and still survives in the cwm.

The rich basic volcanic rocks near Twll Du, the Devil's Kitchen, carry a particularly rich Arctic-Alpine vegetation, including *Saxifraga oppositifolia, Saxifraga hypnoides, Saxifraga stellaris* and *Silene acaulis* and, above all, *Lloydia serotina* which was first found in the Snowdon district by its discoverer, Edward Lhwyd, during the seventeenth century.

Although distributed in the Alps, and in such widely scattered localities as the Himalayas, the Rockies and North Siberia, *Lloydia* occurs nowhere else in Britain outside Snowdonia. Llyn Idwal, unlike most mountain lakes, has a rich organic bottom and carries a number of interesting aquatic plants. Research is being done here by botanists from the Universities of Wales and Cambridge, and also by the Nature Conservancy who are studying the effect of factors such as grazing pressure, differing soils and rainfalls upon vegetation. The mountain birds are those characteristic of Snowdonia and include the Ring Ouzel.

Cwm Idwal is a classic site geologically, and it was here that Darwin, who was originally trained as a geologist, first described the moraines and other glacial relics. He told the story against himself how, in 1831, he and the great geologist, Sedgwick, 'spent many hours in Cwm Idwal examining all the rocks with extreme care . . . but neither of us saw a trace of the wonderful glacial phenomena all around us. We did not notice the plainly scored rocks, the perched boulders, the lateral and terminal moraines, yet these phenomena are so conspicuous that a house burnt down by fire did not tell its story more plainly than did this valley'. It is only too likely that evidence equally plain and equally important is facing us in more than one Nature Reserve, but that, like Darwin in 1831, we are still too blind to read it.

Newborough Warren-Ynys Llanddwyn, Anglesey

NATURE CONSERVANCY RESERVE

6 miles west of Caernarvon: 1,256 acres. Held under leases.
ACCESS. *By rights of way; permits required elsewhere*

LIKE Dungeness and the Axmouth-Lyme Regis Undercliffs, the great sand dunes of Newborough Warren represent one of the most recent transformations of the British coastline. Tidal inundation and sand movement seem to have begun to encroach on the fields of Newborough only just over 600 years ago when 168 acres were destroyed so thoroughly by sea and inthrow of sand as to render it useless for agriculture evermore. For many years before this, the princes of Gwynedd had used the anchorage at Abermenai as their port for voyages to Ireland, but this too became overwhelmed with sand. In 1561 Queen

Elizabeth I instructed the Mayor of Newborough to punish anyone cutting, up-rooting, or carrying away Marram Grass, which was then already being planted to try to arrest the spread of sand. Although so modern physiographically, the Reserve rests on some of the oldest rocks in Britain, those which outcrop at Llanddwyn Island being a variety of metamorphosed rocks of the Gwna Series of the Pre-Cambrian Mona Complex, and including hornblende schist and volcanic rocks interbedded with grits, phyllites, quartzite and limestone.

The scientific interest of this wild tract of sand dunes has been recognised for centuries, and Willoughby and Ray who made two expeditions there in the late seventeenth century discovered there the rare sea Cotton-weed (*Diotis maritima*), which has long since disappeared. A most detailed study of Newborough Warren made during 1950 and 1953 by Dr D. S. Ranwell traces the history of the growth of the dunes and shows that, although they are still advancing inland at over a foot a year, the system as a whole is at present in a relatively stable phase, and this also applies to other dune systems round the coasts of Great Britain. Research is being maintained at Newborough and elsewhere in order to throw light on the cycles of relative stability and instability which these dune systems exhibit. Newborough Warren has also been the scene of particular efforts to map the vegetation, especially of the slacks or hollows left between the new ridges where ground water approaches the sand surface. These slacks are dominated by Creeping Willow (*Salix repens*) and are rich in plants, including some rarities.

The 60-acre island, Ynys Llanddwyn, forms the seaward end of a ridge of rocks underlying the Reserve, and separating the dunes towards the Menai Strait from those on the estuary of the river Cefni. The plants recorded on this island include the Bloody Cranesbill (*Geranium sanguineum*), the Golden Samphire (*Inula crithmoides*) and Sea Spleenwort (*Asplenium marinum*). The Reserve, which has a coastline some eight miles long, is of particular value for the study of stages of sand dune succession, including shifting and fixed dunes. Recent colonisation on the Malltraeth sand by the Sea Poa or Sea Meadowgrass (*Puccinellia maritima*) is the latest of these developments. The Forestry Commission, who have planted much of the inner dunes with trees, have leased the shooting rights over some 2,300 acres to the Nature Conservancy, this area being additional to the 1,256 acres of the Nature Reserve.

Owing to disturbance and the robbing of nests, the former rich bird life had sadly diminished prior to the establishment of the Reserve.

The very rare Roseate Terns were the first to find breeding impossible; and in 1951 when the Common, Arctic and Little Tern tried to breed, something like 200 to 300 pairs of the Common Terns were frustrated by raids on their nests. Two years later both Arctic and Little Terns had given up and all that remained of this once great ternery were fewer than two dozen Common Terns which still managed to nest in a remote corner. Vigorous action was clearly required to restore the position, and in 1955 the Nature Conservancy appointed a whole time Reserve Warden. During the 1956 season several rare birds were able to breed successfully, but the rebuilding of the ternery is bound to be a slow affair, since in contrast to the situation at Ravenglass intervention at Newborough was too late to prevent the continuity of the colony from being interrupted.

Gibraltar Point, Lincolnshire

LOCAL NATURE RESERVE

About 3 miles south of Skegness on the coast: 300 acres.
ACCESS. *Unrestricted*

UNDER the legislation governing Nature Reserves in Great Britain, local authorities (provided that they consult the Nature Conservancy) are as free to establish and manage Nature Reserves as the Conservancy itself. One of the earliest counties to interest itself in such matters was the Lincolnshire (Parts of Lindsey) County Council, which is one of the three administrative counties in Lincolnshire. As far back as 1930 the Council began to consider what they could do to prevent the sand dunes on the Lincolnshire coast being ruined by shack and caravan development. This led in 1932 to the Lindsey County Council (Sandhills) Act, under which the Council bought a considerable area of sand dunes flanking the northern entrance to the Wash, immediately south of Skegness.

Following discussions between the Council and the Lincolnshire Naturalists' Union, the Lincolnshire Naturalists' Trust was created in 1948, and the County Council adopted a scheme delegating to the Trust the management of the property which became the Gibraltar Point Nature Reserve.

In 1949, the Trust established a bird observatory and field research centre, linking the Reserve on the one hand with the chain of East

Coast bird observatories, including Fair Isle, the Isle of May and Spurn Head, and on the other hand with Nottingham University, whose Departments of Geography, Botany and Zoology undertook a series of scientific investigations, including the mapping in great detail of the dunes and the adjoining foreshore. Point was given to these studies of coastal geography, and the County Council's action was fully vindicated, by the North Sea tidal floods of January 31, 1953, when many of the coastal dunes elsewhere, which had unwisely been built over or trampled down and eroded by holiday-makers, were immediately breached causing great losses and destruction, while the carefully conserved dune system of Gibraltar Point stood up to the assault and helped to protect Skegness from the disasters which overtook some of the communities farther north.

Aided by this object lesson, the County Council successfully appealed to the Minister for the right to prevent the encroachment of a caravan settlement on a site immediately adjoining Gibraltar Point Nature Reserve by means of a compulsory purchase order, the only one so far to be made under the 1949 Act. Other extensions are being completed. The Skegness Urban District Council also agreed informally to bring its dunes under the management of the Lincolnshire Naturalists' Trust so far as nature conservation and research are concerned, under the title 'The Skegness Nature Reserve'. In 1952 Gibraltar Point became the first Local Nature Reserve under the 1949 Act to be declared in England. Byelaws were also made for the protection of the Reserve. The original bird observatory rapidly extended to serve as a forward base for work on marine biology, physiography, botany and other branches of zoology. Nottingham University have announced their intention of using the field laboratories here for the study of maritime communities and of land formation and land stabilisation.

It is encouraging to observe that all this pioneering activity has been carried through without the necessity for any national organisation to lend more than background encouragement and support. Such initiative on the spot helps not only to extend but to diversify and enrich the common fund of experience about ecological field studies and Nature Reserve management.

The extensive foreshore and intertidal zone forms a rich feeding area and a quiet roost for many sea and shore birds, including on migration hundreds of Terns, Kittiwakes, waders such as Knot sometimes in flocks of up to 10,000, Whimbrel, Bar-tailed Godwits, Pink-footed Geese and some Whooper Swans, Arctic Skuas, Divers and occasional rare visitors. Beyond the shore are the mobile and fixed dunes colonised by a succession of plants, including fine thickets of Sea Buckthorn (*Hippophae rhamnoides*), with its bright orange berries, and also Dewberry (*Rubus caesius*), Elder, Privet and Hawthorn.

Near the tip of the dunes is the Bird Observatory with its large Heligoland Trap, a high cage into which birds are carefully driven in order to be caught, marked with metal rings and released. More than a thousand, of over 50 species, are ringed at the Observatory every year and some extremely interesting results have been obtained, including a Redwing ringed at the Observatory during its first winter and found dying in Cyprus the following winter, while another Redwing was found at Taranto in south Italy the winter after ringing. One of the extraordinary features of coastal bird migration at Gibraltar Point is that it is in the same direction both in Spring and Autumn, from the north to south and south-west.

Behind the growing sand dune ridges are a series of salt marshes dominated by Glasswort (*Salicornia*), Sea Grass (*Glyceria*), Sea Lavender (*Limonium*), Sea Purslane (*Halimione*), and Couch Grass (*Agropyron*). These marshes contain many interesting plants and are also favoured by birds such as wintering Shore-larks. As many as 140 species of birds have been seen in the Nature Reserve in one year.

Humber Wildfowl Refuge, Yorkshire and Lincolnshire

STATUTORY BIRD SANCTUARY

Situated between Brough and Trent Falls on the Humber: some 20 sq. miles. Administered by the Humber Wildfowl Refuge Committee. ACCESS. Limited to essential permit holders

WHILE many nature reserves are places of great beauty and varied scientific interest, there are cases in which it is necessary to give protection to species such as ducks and geese on whatever wild and featureless expanses they may choose for roosting and feeding. Such Refuges may be effective only during a part of the year when they are used by migratory wildfowl. They may even be effective during only part of the 24 hours and be covered by high tide for the remainder, yet they can play a great part, particularly in hard weather, in enabling a

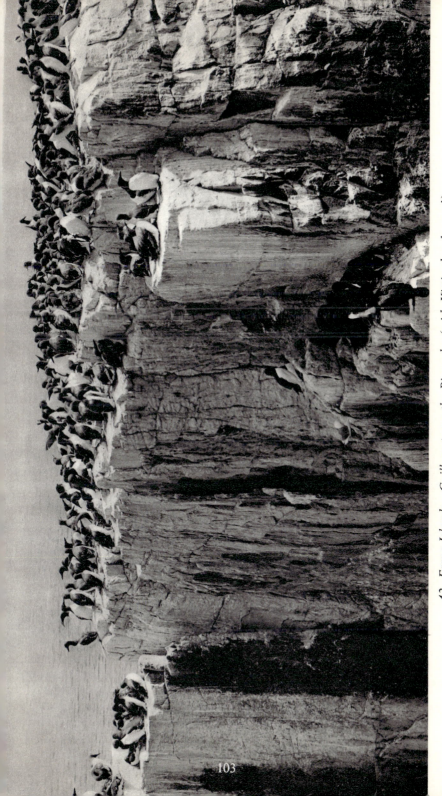

42. *Farne Islands. Guillemots on the Pinnacles (with Kittiwakes beneath).*

43. *Grey Seals on Shillay, Outer Hebrides. The two extreme left animals, near and far, are bulls; the rest cows and pups.*

sufficient stock of birds to survive for the next breeding season, and in encouraging birds to stay in areas from which persecution would soon drive them away, possibly for ever. As holding grounds and reservoirs they therefore serve to maintain the bird population over very much wider regions, and they can make all the difference between extinction and survival for northern breeding species whose wintering grounds are steadily being reduced by the inroads of civilisation.

The best example of this sort in Great Britain is the Humber Wildfowl Refuge established in 1955. It extends over some 20 square miles of tidal flats and water on the Upper Humber between Brough and Trent Falls. Its main purpose is to protect the Humber roosting grounds of the Pink-footed Goose and, incidentally, to afford a refuge to large numbers of ducks and waders. During the first season the Pink-footed Geese arrived in large numbers in the early autumn, but most of them did not stay through the whole winter, partly owing to the severe weather. Wigeon and other duck remained on the Refuge in enormous numbers and quickly learnt where they were safe.

One of the interesting and new features of this Refuge is that it is supervised by a joint committee of naturalists and sportsmen with the support of the Nature Conservancy and the Humber Conservancy Board. During the first season a wildfowler, Mr L. T. Field, J.P., acted as chairman and the unanimity and keenness of the committee showed how great are the possibilities of joint action for conservation. All the year round honorary wardens keep watch on the Refuge, and throughout the important winter roosting period the Nature Conservancy provide a full-time warden. This was the first example of a new Refuge created under the Sanctuaries clause of the Protection of Birds Act, 1954.

Farndale, Yorkshire

LOCAL NATURE RESERVE

3 miles north of Kirkby Moorside: 2,500 acres. ACCESS. *Local voluntary wardens advise on access*

EVERY spring people come from long distances to admire the finest display of wild Daffodils in England in the upper valley of the River Dove in the Yorkshire North Riding, which is known as Farndale and runs down to Kirkby Moorside. For years the Ryedale branch of the

K

Council for the Preservation of Rural England struggled by voluntary means to preserve the Daffodils from wanton destruction and to persuade visitors to respect this annual display of rare natural beauty.

In April, 1952, officers of rambling clubs, the Youth Hostels Association, and the Cyclists' Touring Club joined in an appeal to visitors 'to allow all to share in the unsullied and untrampled beauty of the wild flowers in their natural state' and asked town-dwellers to assist by refusing to buy the little bunches of dying wild Daffodils that were hawked from door to door by itinerant vendors. In 1953 a hundred and three members of the Ryedale branch of the C.P.R.E. voluntarily worked in shifts to prevent visitors from picking and destroying flowers, but even this great effort did not prove adequate in the absence of legal authority.

In 1955, therefore, the North Riding County Council, after consultation with the Nature Conservancy, declared 2,500 acres of Farndale a Nature Reserve for the specific purpose of protecting the Daffodils, and made a byelaw setting a penalty of £5 for uprooting, cutting or wilfully or negligently injuring any Daffodil, Narcissus, or the bulb, stem, flower or leaf thereof within the Farndale Nature Reserve. Local farmers, and other residents who had suffered from the raids of Daffodil looters, were enthusiastic for the Nature Reserve. One farmer remarked how glad he was that people could be stopped from picking the flowers ruthlessly. 'A few we wouldn't mind,' he said, 'but they break fences and leave gates open and in the morning there is a trail of dead flowers everywhere and endless litter'. He spoke of visitors in their hundreds and roads packed with cars nose to tail.

During the new Nature Reserve's first season wardens with bright yellow arm-bands and official cards were out in forces ranging from about a dozen on Saturdays to as many as 30 on Sundays and on Easter Monday. The Head Warden was the Area Planning Officer for the North Riding County Council. The wardens included local members of the Council for the Preservation of Rural England and members of rambling and Youth Hostels Associations, Senior Scouts and Guides as well as schoolmasters and students. Green notice boards were placed at the approaches to Farndale informing visitors that they were entering a Nature Reserve and the police gave considerable backing, besides operating a one-way traffic system made necessary by the number of buses, cars, motor cyclists and cyclists. On the peak Sunday the number of visitors was estimated at about 8,000. It was only necessary to prosecute five offenders, all of whom were fined.

44. *Roudsea Wood Nature Reserve; sea-shore meeting Oak Wood.*

45. *Moor House Nature Reserve. Looking west over Field Station to Great Dun Fell. Little Dun Fell and Cross Fell (2,930 ft.).*

46. *Moor House*
Nature Reserve.
The Reserve sign
by Moss Burn.
Great Dun Fell
and Little Dun Fell
in background.

These energetic methods proved highly successful and fully justified the establishment of the largest Local Nature Reserve so far created, and the only one which exists solely for the preservation of wild flowers.

Farne Islands, Northumberland

NATIONAL TRUST RESERVE

Some 15 miles south-east of Berwick: 80 acres. ACCESS. *Controlled*

SPECTACULAR colonies of seals and of sea-birds appeal to almost everyone. The Farnes have the added asset of spectacular scenery as their columnar and deeply fissured cliffs of quartz dolerite rise abruptly out of the North Sea. Although landing is possible only in fairly good weather, the Farnes are among the most accessible as well as the most attractive of uninhabited islands. Their numbers and area are largely a matter of opinion, depending on the state of the tides, but up to 28 are distinguished, the largest being the Inner Farne with a low water extent of about 16 acres.

The first man to protect the wild life on the Farnes was St Cuthbert, who moved there for the sake of solitude nearly 1,300 years ago. During the nineteenth century visitors to the islands committed great destruction and many acts of cruelty among the wild life. After a brief struggle to improve matters by Archdeacon Thorp in the middle of the nineteenth century, the Farne Islands Association was formed to guard the islands through watchers during the 1880s. In 1925 the islands were bought through a public appeal and handed over to the National Trust to be maintained permanently as a bird sanctuary, four watchers being regularly employed during the breeding season. The value of this protection was shown during the Second World War when it was temporarily interrupted and much damage was done by raiding parties as well as some by enemy bombs. Few Nature Reserves anywhere have had so long or so eventful a history as the Farnes.

This history is well illustrated by the most famous bird of the Farnes, which until recently bred nowhere else in England—the Eider Duck, long known as St Cuthbert's duck and reputed to have been first protected by him. Medieval records show how tame these birds were during the twelfth to fourteenth centuries. After bad setbacks following the Napoleonic Wars and again about 1870, the number of nests gradually rose to several hundreds before the Second World War. In 1942 they were reduced to not more than about 130 on all the islands combined, but through special efforts the numbers were restored to well over 500 by 1955.

The Farnes are also notable as a breeding place of Terns. Sandwich Terns had a large breeding colony there before 1831, but owing to persecution they deserted temporarily to Coquet Island. History repeated itself in 1922 when they were much harried by visitors and robbed of their eggs. They gave up attempting to breed in the middle of June, some of them possibly shifting to the Norfolk sanctuaries which were better protected at that time. In 1939 a peak of about 2,000 pairs was reached, but numbers collapsed during the war. Fortunately, under renewed protection, they had risen again by 1955 to some 1,500 pairs. The rare Roseate Tern has had a similar history of fluctuations but at a far lower level, often only two or three pairs. Recent protection has raised their numbers to something approaching 100 pairs. Arctic Terns have on the Farnes their most southerly important colony, which appears often to exceed 3,000 pairs.

Perhaps even more spectacular than the Terns are the Puffins, which nest in burrows in thousands. The Guillemots which are also numerous are scientifically interesting as they belong to a different sub-species from the colony at St Abb's Head in Scotland, only some 30 miles farther north, this being the line of division between the two geographical races. Only a handful of Razorbills breed. The graceful Kittiwake has bred on the Farnes at least since the time of Ray (1678) and several hundred pairs now breed. They have been the subject of intense scientific study and a remarkable number of those which have been ringed have crossed the Atlantic to Newfoundland, Labrador, Southern Greenland or even the Azores.

One of the principal management problems has long been the control of numbers of the larger gulls which raid the eggs of other species and kill young birds and even adults of such species as the Puffin. During the nineteenth century the Lesser Black-backs enormously outnumbered the equally troublesome Herring Gulls, but recently the proportion of the two species has been more even, sometimes one being more numerous and sometimes the other.

The Grey Seals on the Farne Islands, which used to be severely persecuted, have increased greatly under protection, and numbers have been estimated to approach 3,000, compared with about 100 during the late nineteenth and early twentieth century. These seals are the cause of one of the few territorial conflicts between Scotland and England, the English (including both naturalists and fishermen) being on their side, while the Scots bring bitter complaints of damage to their salmon fisheries, especially at the mouth of the Tweed. In spite of the immense difficulties involved, considerable numbers of young have been captured, measured, weighed and marked with metal tags and some have been recovered as far away as Norway and Germany within a few weeks of leaving their birth-place for the first time. The calves are born between the end of October and Christmas. Durham Cathedral Library contains a Charter regulating the killing of seals here as long ago as the twelfth century.

Rabbits are common on the islands, but are heavily interbred with domesticated stock. This is one of the few Nature Reserves on which rabbit populations can be maintained without fear of their infesting agricultural and forest land.

The plant life is very limited, and no fewer than 16 species are known to have disappeared during the last 100 years.

Roudsea Wood, Lancashire

NATURE CONSERVANCY RESERVE

About 10 miles west of Grange-over-Sands: 287 acres. Part under Nature Reserve Agreement and part leased from Mr R. E. O. Cavendish. ACCESS. *Permits required for whole Reserve*

IF BRITAIN were like some other countries—fairly uniform over its whole extent—a comprehensive system of Nature Reserves for purposes of conservation and research would only need to include a fairly limited number of sites, but Britain probably includes a wider variety of soils, climates, vegetation and animal communities within a small area than almost any other country on earth, and this diversity of conditions can only be done justice by a fairly extensive range of Nature Reserves. These, moreover, must exhibit the differing effects of past treatments and interferences by man, as well as the differences arising naturally.

Roudsea Wood illustrates this point very well and was chosen because of the astonishing range of different conditions exhibited in less than 300 acres. Two low ridges, one of Carboniferous Limestone and the other of Silurian Bannisdale Slates, form the main part of the Reserve, divided by a shallow valley. The eastern fringe is formed by a typical moss or flat peat moor. On the north flows the river Leven, on the west is farmland, and to the south-west the oak wood passes through a rapid transition into salt marsh fringing the extensive tidal flats of the Leven estuary.

Along the limestone ridge grow Yews, flanked by Oak and Ash and carpeted in May by the flowers of Lilies of the Valley. On the slate grows a typical Lake District oakwood which used to be managed as coppice but has been allowed to come up again to high forest during the past half century. Estate records and maps going back more than 100 years show how the former Roudsea tarn has become overgrown and filled up. The tarn is still interesting for its insects and plants, among which is the Yellow Sedge (*Carex flava*), which grows nowhere else in Britain. Some of the wood has a south-country richness about it, and this impression is helped by the amount of Hazel coppice and the occurrence of Lime (*Tilia cordata*), Spindle, Buckthorn, Dogwood and Guelder Rose. The Oaks are mainly sessile. Among the other trees are Alder, some Scots Pine, Sycamore, Birch, Wych Elm, Holly, Hawthorn and Rowan.

The variety of the Reserve is further illustrated by the list of birds, including (on the adjoining flats) Oystercatcher, Curlew, Ringed Plover and a number of breeding pairs of Shelduck, while in contrast the wood contains such species as Bullfinch, Wood Warbler, Jay, Tawny Owl, Woodcock and Nightjar, Willow Warblers being the commonest breeding birds. Among mammals, Roe Deer are notable.

For research purposes Roudsea Wood is being developed as a north-country counterpart to Wytham Wood in the sense that the programme envisages a comprehensive inventory of its plant and animal life, including even the most obscure invertebrates. Studies already carried out cover millipedes and centipedes, ants, Hemiptera (plant bugs), slugs and snails and several other groups. This is also the scene of some of the Nature Conservancy's studies on the breakdown of litter and of the associated fauna, which involves analysing the nutrients in the litter and how they are used as the first stage in the pyramid of animal life which is based on woodland. Techniques of assessing populations of invertebrates are also being tested here and comparative studies are being made of different methods of forest regeneration, including the effects of attacks by the caterpillars of *Tortrix viridana* on the supply of acorns.

The rainfall is between 50 and 60 inches, much higher than that a

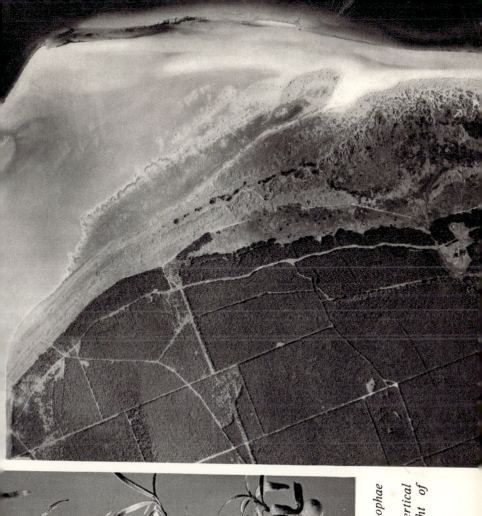

47. Aberlady Bay. Sea Buckthorn (Hippophae rhamnoides).

48. Tentsmuir Point Nature Reserve. Vertical view showing coastal accretion to right of Tentsmuir Forest.

49. *Morton Lochs Nature Reserve from the air.*

few miles to the east, but much lower than that of the central Lake District to the north.

Most of the wood is managed on an agreed silvicultural plan by the landowner, Mr R. E. O. Cavendish, and it is within the limits of the Lake District National Park.

Moor House, Westmorland

NATURE CONSERVANCY RESERVE

Forms the north-east corner of Westmorland: 10,000 *acres.*
ACCESS. *By Pennine Way; permits required elsewhere*

As THE high Pennines approach their northern end towards the Roman Wall they show an impressive escarpment facing south-west across the fertile Eden valley towards the Lake Distict, culminating in Cross Fell whose summit is only 70 feet below the 3,000-foot contour. Straddling the ridge immediately southward and extending far down the bleak moorland slopes to the east is the 10,000-acre Nature Reserve of Moor House, whose northern and eastern boundary follows the Tees from its source below Cross Fell to within two miles of Cauldron Snout.

The mountain mass is built up of many thin beds of Carboniferous Limestone, shale and sandstone, arranged in a recurring pattern. The limestone beds include many mineral veins, some of them rich in lead which was extensively worked in the eighteenth and early nineteenth centuries. Barytes and fluorspar are still being extracted. Almost all the rock is capped by boulder clay or solifluxion deposits, and these again are hidden almost entirely beneath a thick blanket of peat, varying in depth up to 14 feet. Up to altitudes of about 2,400 feet the basal layers of the peat often contain the stumps of trees, some of them quite large. They are relics of a period more than 6,000 years ago, when the climate was probably warmer and less favourable to the growth of peat bogs than that of the succeeding millennia. Signs of human occupation at these high altitudes, and the remains of wild cattle, also suggest a less inhospitable environment during that phase of pre-history.

The present-day climate, which we may take to have been broadly similar for at least 2,000 years, can reasonably be described as severe, and has been compared to that at sea level in Iceland. A typical Spring month, April, 1956, showed a daily mean minimum temperature of 3½°F below freezing point. It rained on 20 days, snowed on 8, hailed on 4, gave fog on 4 and ground frost on 25, and the temperature never exceeded 52° although the average daily sunshine was as high as 4·7 hours. Ground frost occurred on 13 days in May and on 3 even in June. In July 7 inches of rain fell in about 103 hours. The average wind force at Moor House is about 15 miles per hour.

Although the extent and thickness of peat bog may be ascribed to the nature of the climate, yet the detailed character of the peat vegetation and of the landscape as a whole as we see it to-day is a monument to human ignorance and mismanagement. Mining, for example, has left spoil heaps which even a century later remain toxic to vegetation and animal life. Centuries of sheep grazing have destroyed the woodland which even under the present climate could have occupied the steeper, and therefore better drained, slopes of the valley-sides and the more fertile alluvial soils of the broader valley bottoms.

Overgrazing has spoilt the quality of the grassland which replaced these trees, so that the ground has been taken over by poor and rank moorland plants. Burning of the peat bog has largely dissipated such potential fertility as it may once have possessed, and has encouraged its natural tendency to erosion. As a result, much of the peat blanket is now heavily eroded. Between the wasting mounds of peat, crowned by a disintegrating mat of scrubby heaths and lichens, the steep-sided channels meander through crumbling banks—a land-surface heartbreaking to traverse, and useless to man or beast.

The main object of the Moor House Reserve and Field Station is not to conserve rare plants and animals, but to carry out an intensive long-term study of the almost unknown conditions of life in highland Britain. Among researches in progress are the measurement of run-off of water from areas of natural and artificially drained bog, observations on the effects of grazing on the vegetation and on the possibilities of restoring higher grades of vegetation by giving temporary protection from grazing pressure, attempts to renew the growth at high altitudes of trees, such as Birch, Scots Pine, Rowan and Bird Cherry, and experiments in diversifying moorland vegetation and arresting the deterioration of peat by planting selected species on experimental plots.

This research programme is being assisted by a number of authorities interested in high altitudes, including the Wear & Tees River Board, the Meteorological Office, the Forestry Commission, the University of Durham and a number of agricultural organisations. While it will

50. *Cairngorms Naure Reserve. Cairn Toul and Sgar an Lochan Uaine (Angel's Peak). View from Coire Bhrochain of Braeriach.*

51 Cairngorms Nature Reserve. Rothiemurchus Forest. One of the many peaty lochans in the natural forest of Scots Pine.

probably be a long time before full-scale results are obtained, the early indications suggest that much can be done in highland Britain to improve fertility and shelter not only for plants and wild animals, but also as a source of wealth and of relief from over-pressure on our limited land resources. Moor House should help us to understand how these wild tracts of moorland have come to deteriorate so gravely, how to up-grade their soil fertility and how to restore, as closely as we can, the natural vegetation and wild life.

Ravenglass, Cumberland

LOCAL NATURE RESERVE

14½ miles west of Coniston: 583 acres. ACCESS. *Permits required during period April 15–July 15 each year*

BETWEEN the highest Lakeland mountains and the sea three little rivers, Esk, Irt and Mite, flow together near the village of Ravenglass on the Cumberland coast. Protecting the estuaries from the sea is a line of sand dunes, about two miles long and up to half a mile broad, which was one of the first places in England to become famous as a bird sanctuary, thanks to the careful guardianship of the Muncaster Castle Estate and the work of some of the early bird photographers. The Rev. Cecil F. Tomlinson, writing in the *Naturalist* for 1934, mentions a visit to Ravenglass sanctuary in 1893 when the keeper showed him with great pride about half a dozen nests of Sandwich Terns. These Terns had begun to breed at Ravenglass before 1887 and they built up a colony of about 100 pairs in the first decade of this century, collapsing to under 20 pairs between 1915 and 1930 and rising again to at least 365 pairs in 1932.

Historically, the backbone of the ternery has consisted of Common Terns, although Arctics are said to have been equal in numbers about a hundred years ago, but it is difficult to be sure so far back that the identifications were correct. Here in Cumberland the Arctic Tern is near the southern limit of its breeding range and records of breeding at Ravenglass ceased about 1920, although some nests were reported again during the 'thirties. Even the Common Terns failed to breed between 1913 and 1917; Little Terns bred in smaller but probably more constant numbers.

L

Perhaps even more celebrated than the ternery is the great colony of Black-headed Gulls which overlaps the same breeding area but also extends farther north along the dunes. In the 1938 survey of Black-headed Gull colonies Ravenglass was credited with 'some tens of thousands of breeding pairs, probably less than fifty thousand'. Critical review ten years later indicated that this estimate provided by the local watchers was considerably above the mark, and that about ten thousand pairs was the probable population; even this still means that nearly one-third of all Black-headed Gulls breeding in England were concentrated at Ravenglass.

During the Second World War the carefully built-up protection of the colony and the farming of the Black-headed Gulls' eggs by taking a toll which did not reduce the breeding population met a disastrous setback. In 1941, during the national food shortage, probably about 73,000 eggs were collected, which was far more than the colony could stand. The ending of the war aggravated, rather than relieved, the problem, since Ravenglass found itself sandwiched between the gunnery range at Eskmeals and the atomic development at Sellafield. Despite a Sanctuary Order under the Wild Birds Protection Act, the eggs were heavily raided. The Muncaster Castle Estate concluded in 1951 that it was no longer within their power to continue the responsibility for protection.

A spirited local meeting took place on May 21, 1953, at which the whole problem was discussed and general support was expressed for the creation of a Local Nature Reserve. The Cumberland County Council followed up the business with the greatest vigour and efficiency and in March, 1954, Drigg Warren, near Ravenglass, was officially declared by the County Council as the Drigg Dunes and Gullery Nature Reserve, near Ravenglass, the area actually being in Drigg parish. In April, byelaws were made giving full protection to animals and plants in the Reserve and restricting entry during the breeding season to permit-holders. Mr Joe Farren, who had for some 50 years watched over the colony, became the principal warden and was supported by eight others —seven being volunteers. All this was made possible by a Nature Reserve Agreement with Major G. W. Pennington, owner of the Muncaster Estate.

The response of the birds was immediate. Sandwich Terns, which had previously been reduced to a few dozens, increased to an estimated strength of between three and four hundred pairs. Public support was excellent. In 1955, 15 wardens looked after the colony and 77 permits were issued to see it, nine of which were for school parties. Well over a thousand pairs of Terns bred, including 480 Sandwich; the Black-headed Gulls also increased in numbers.

Ravenglass was the scene of considerable early bird-marking activity and in 1954 a Common Tern was recovered there which had been ringed as a young bird 25 years earlier—the oldest wild ringed bird so far recorded in England.

Ravenglass has also recently been chosen for some important research into bird behaviour under the supervision of Dr N. Tinbergen of Oxford University, in which zoologists from several different countries have collaborated.

The successful transformation of this long established and jealously guarded private sanctuary into a well-managed statutory Nature Reserve with continuity of wardening is one of the most successful chapters in the history of British nature conservation.

Aberlady Bay, East Lothian

LOCAL NATURE RESERVE

On the south side of the Firth of Forth between Edinburgh and North Berwick: 1,439 acres. ACCESS. *Unrestricted*

ABERLADY BAY in East Lothian became on July 14, 1952, the first Local Nature Reserve to be declared in Great Britain under the National Parks and Access to the Countryside Act, 1949, being ahead of Gibraltar Point in Lincolnshire by just over a fortnight. Unfortunately, the misunderstandings between wildfowlers and bird protectionists, which had at that time become chronic, resulted in a determined campaign by local wildfowlers to upset on legal grounds the byelaws made for the protection of the Reserve by the East Lothian County Council. After prolonged controversy the case finally went to the High Court of Justiciary in Edinburgh, which on March 24, 1955, upheld the legality of the byelaws and in effect ruled that wildfowling could not be continued within the Nature Reserve without a permit under the byelaws.

It has been the policy of the County Council to issue a few shooting permits for Mallard and Wigeon only, and although this has been regretted by many protectionists, it has not created sufficient disturbance of the Reserve to discourage the Pink-footed Geese and other birds, which had previously abandoned the area, from returning to it. A small colony of Common, Arctic and Little Terns has had very limited breeding success in spite of the determined attempts at protection.

This sheltered bay is a favoured haunt of rare ducks, waders and migratory small birds, and is also botanically interesting. Dense thickets of Sea Buckthorn grow to a remarkable height. In addition to being a favourite resort Aberlady is considerably used for teaching and demonstration purposes and the County Council's initiative in establishing the Nature Reserve has been fully justified.

Isle of May, Fife

NATURE CONSERVANCY RESERVE

At mouth of Firth of Forth, some 5 miles south-east of Anstruther: 140 acres. Under Nature Reserve Agreement with the Commissioners of Northern Lighthouses. ACCESS. *Intending visitors should apply to the Nature Conservancy, 12 Hope Terrace, Edinburgh, 9*

WHILE several Scottish islands of great scientific importance can only be reached by long and perilous journeys, the Isle of May is so placed in the entry to the Firth of Forth that the smoke of Edinburgh can be seen from it on a clear day. It is a mile-long exposure of a sill of analcite-dolerite rock with columnar structure, pointing from northwest to south-east and covering 143 acres. The south-western cliffs are 160 feet high. The earliest lighthouse in Scotland was on the Isle of May and at the present time the lighthouse keepers and their wives are the only inhabitants, together with one goat and a few sheep. Rabbits overran the island until myxomatosis arrived (probably introduced by a gull in March, 1955), since when their population has been reduced to very small numbers. The only other mammals are House Mice and visiting Grey Seals.

The plants, although not including any rarities, are interesting because they have been rather carefully recorded over a long period during which certain species such as the Yellow Stonecrop (*Sedum acre*) and the Oyster Plant (*Mertensia maritima*) have died out, while other species have arrived, possibly introduced in the droppings of the numerous gulls. The original lighthouse burnt coal in quantities of up to three tons nightly, with the result that a vast cinder heap covers much of the island

and affects its vegetation. The island is treeless except for a few bushes of Spruce, Sycamore and Elder.

The main interest is in the migratory and breeding birds. The migrants, which have been studied for 50 years, first of all by Miss Baxter and Miss Rintoul and subsequently by the Isle of May Bird Observatory and Field Station, include immense numbers of the normal migrants across the North Sea and among them occasional rarities such as the Black-headed, Yellow-breasted and Rustic Buntings (*Emberiza melanocephala, E. aureola* and *E. rustica*), the Isabelline Shrike (*Lanius isabellinus*), the Siberian Thrush (*Turdus sibiricus*), the Pied and Black-eared Wheat-ears (*Oenanthe leucomela* and *O. hispanica*), and the Subalpine Warbler (*Sylvia cantillans*). How such Asiatic and Mediterranean species wander here is a mystery which is only gradually being solved by the work of the bird observatories. Bluethroats, Scarlet Grosbeaks and Red-breasted Flycatchers are among the rather more frequent rarities.

Thirty-seven species are known to have nested on the island at one time or another since 1710, seven of them once only and two others, the Gannet and the Cormorant, for a brief period. Four species have ceased to breed, including the Black Guillemot, which is everywhere receding northwards and westwards, and the Tree Sparrow, which for some reason used to breed commonly on many islands, including St Kilda, which it has subsequently deserted. The others are the Rock Dove, also a declining species, and the Peregrine. The compensating gains—if they can be termed compensating—include the Carrion Crow, the Herring and Lesser Black-backed Gulls and the Fulmar. Herring Gulls have increased from one breeding pair in 1907 and about 450 in 1936 to about 3,000 at the present time, despite attempts to control their numbers. Lesser Black-backs, which began breeding only in 1930, rose to about 75 pairs by 1946 and between 250 and 300 in 1955. Fulmars started breeding in 1930 and although 30 pairs now attempt to rear young, nine is the largest number they have succeeded in bringing off. Shags, which had only two or three pairs for over a century up to the 1930s, have now increased to over 200, and Oystercatchers have also increased, although at a much lower level. Puffins are dwindling, and in 1955 prob-ably did not exceed seven pairs.

Four species of Terns nest in widely fluctuating numbers, Common Terns having ranged up to 5,000 pairs or more in 1946-7 and Arctic Terns up to between 400 and 550 in 1946, while Sandwich Terns have fluctuated between four and 1,500 pairs. Roseate Terns do not nest regularly, although a few have done so recently. Fortunately there are no rats on the island, but it is feared that the enormous numbers of large gulls are not helpful to other breeding species.

The Nature Reserve was established in 1956 by agreement with the Commissioners of Northern Lighthouses, who own the island, and its management will be undertaken in co-operation with the Committee representing the Scottish Universities, the Midlothian Ornithological Club and the Commissioners of Northern Lighthouses, which has for some years supervised the bird observatory.

Tentsmuir Point and Morton Lochs, Fife

NATURE CONSERVANCY RESERVE

In north-west Fife: 151 *acres.* ACCESS. *To Tentsmuir unrestricted. Permits to visit required for Morton Lochs*

IMMEDIATELY south of the mouth of the Tay and north of the Eden, which reaches the sea near St Andrews, is a broad strip of sandy ground, until recently wild and open, but largely covered since 1922 by some thousands of acres of conifers. Two small parts of this rich and interesting area have been secured as National Nature Reserves. The first, known as Tentsmuir Point, includes a series of sand-dunes with intervening slacks and a gently sloping foreshore, which is still below high-water mark but is rapidly growing from accretion and from the processes of dune formation and dune colonisation.

The new dunes are colonised in the usual order by *Agropyron*, *Elymus* and *Ammophila* or Marram Grass. These help to fix the sand partly by binding it and partly by slowing down the speed of wind blowing over its surface. Behind them are wet slacks, calcareous because of the high shell content of the sand, which in the late summer are white with the lovely flowers of the Grass of Parnassus (*Parnassia palustris*). Among other interesting flowers of the Reserve are the Coral-root Orchid (*Corallorhiza trifida*), whose roots actually look like pieces of white coral, the Lesser Twayblade (*Listera cordata*), the Moonwort (*Botrychium lunaria*) and the Curved Sedge (*Carex maritima*). The Seaside Centaury (*Centaurium littorale*), which was discovered here in 1937, is a rare plant on the east coast of Scotland.

The Reserve is a useful roost and refuge for sea and shore birds and Roe Deer out of the adjoining forest sometimes come right out on to the foreshore. The Reserve was formed by exchange with the Forestry Commission for a former bird sanctuary nearby which had become unsuitable owing to changed conditions.

The Morton Lochs Nature Reserve, just under three miles from the North Sea, consists of some small artificial lochs and surrounding rough wet land. They were created towards the end of the last century for trout fishing, but proved extremely attractive to water birds as they lie near the junction of two important migration routes, one following the coast south and the other turning inland by the Firth of Tay and Loch Leven. Increased disturbance gradually diminished the attraction, which it is now sought to restore by keeping the area very quiet and by confining observation to carefully placed observation posts, used only when necessary. It has also been necessary to restore control of the water level. Among birds visiting the lochs are the Whooper Swan and the Little Gull, which occurs more frequently between the Tay and the Forth than anywhere else in Great Britain.

Ben Lawers, Perthshire

A Property of the NATIONAL TRUST FOR SCOTLAND

On north side of Loch Tay: 8,000 *acres.* ACCESS. *Unrestricted*

NO OTHER mountain in Great Britain as high as Ben Lawers lies so far south. The Trust have recently replaced by a small cairn and indicator, the ruined earlier summit cairn which had been intended to give it the necessary additional 16 feet of height to reach the 4,000-foot contour. This great height is fully appreciated from the other side of Loch Tay which lies at its foot, only about a dozen miles from the beginning of the low plains near Crieff. The many mountains to the west of it help to reduce its rainfall and during the latter part of the winter it is often covered by a blanket of snow which makes it a popular place for skiers.

Geologically it is composed of Dalradian schists, which are Pre-Cambrian sedimentary rocks metamorphosed at a stage when they were exposed to high temperatures and high shearing pressures within the earth's crust, long before they were upthrust and then denuded to their present state. Finally, glaciers of the Ice Age deposited a residue of drift, found principally on the south-eastern side below 2,600 feet.

The geology, botany and zoology of Ben Lawers have been excellently described and illustrated in *Ben Lawers and its Alpine Flowers* (published at 4s. by the National Trust for Scotland, 5 Charlotte Square, Edinburgh 2). Dr Duncan Poore has traced in this booklet some of the reasons why Ben Lawers is one of the most famous places for Alpine plants in Great Britain and is visited by botanists even from the Alps of Europe and from America. He suggests that the woodland which must once have covered the southern slopes of these hills consisted mainly of Oak, Birch, Alder, Willows and at the highest levels Birch and Rowan. The present vegetation derives from forest clearance and grazing pressure, aided by the comparatively low rainfall, by snow cover and by the exposure to wind with varying degrees of shelter and shade and, above all, from the mineral richness constantly replenished by the breakdown of more of the parent rock.

Among the rare and beautiful plants of Ben Lawers are the *Saxifraga cernua*, which was discovered here in 1790 and was long thought to be found nowhere else, and the Alpine Forget-me-not (*Myosotis alpestris*). The animals of Ben Lawers are less notable, but Ptarmigan and Mountain Hares are found on the higher slopes, and Wild Cats are occasionally seen.

Ben Lawers and surrounding mountains were purchased by the National Trust for Scotland in 1950. One of the main aims is to ensure the preservation of the rare Alpine flora. Ben Lawers can, therefore, be regarded as a Nature Reserve and visitors to the mountain are expressly urged not to collect these plants or to uproot them as specimens.

Cairngorms, Inverness-shire & Aberdeenshire

NATURE CONSERVANCY RESERVE

39,689 acres. Part owned; the remainder under Nature Reserve Agreements with Lt.-Col. J. P. Grant, the Trustees of the late Duke of Fife, and Major J. H. Drake. ACCESS. *Unrestricted*

HIGH barren mountains exposed to all kinds of weather are among the few habitats which have resisted up to now almost every form of human exploitation and injury. Scenically they offer some of the most spectacular settings for Nature Reserves, while scientifically they enable us to study the limiting conditions for distribution of animals and plants and the evolution of landscape and soils from the solid geology under the influence of climatic extremes. In addition to forming the

52. *Cairngorms Nature Reserve. Rothiemurchus Forest. Scots Pine, Juniper, Calluna dominant.*

53. *Glen Derry in the Cairngorms. Climbers reading Reserve sign, headed by the Scottish Crown.*

specialised habitat of many interesting plants and animals, they also, by their inaccessibility, provide the last refuge for a number of species which used to be more widely distributed. These are only some of the reasons why adequate representation of mountain country must figure prominently in any comprehensive programme of Nature Reserves, especially for a largely mountainous island such as Great Britain.

The 40,000-acre Cairngorms Nature Reserve, rising at several points above the 4,000-foot contour, is the principal mountain area among the British Nature Reserves. It contains many bleak and exposed summits with snow patches which lie nearly all the year, and with waterfalls and torrents, small rivers, lochans and lochs, precipices, crags and screes, stony plateaus, arctic-alpine heaths, high moorlands, grasslands, pine heaths and pine forest and other habitat types and stages, all on such a scale that even an active and skilful naturalist would take several weeks to acquire even an elementary knowledge of the whole Reserve.

It is now 137 years since that great Scottish naturalist William Macgillivray, later Professor of Natural History at Aberdeen, crossed the high mountains on his way home as a poor student and made probably the first plant list of the area, after a cold and uncomfortable night on the mountains. Although many naturalists have worked in the area since, much remains to be learnt about the fauna and flora and also about the mountain climate, which is the subject of specialised studies by the Nature Conservancy and by Aberdeen University, particularly relating to snow, evaporation, temperature and rainfall. This is one of the few parts of Britain where snow has important effects on vegetation and these are being studied by measurements of the depth and duration of snow cover.

More than 200 species of flowering plants are found in the Reserve. J. Grant Roger has stated that most of the 75 British arctic-alpine species occur in the Cairngorms, including the very local Whortle-leaved Willow (*Salix myrsinites*), the Alpine Mouse-ear Chickweed (*Cerastium alpinum*), the Purple Saxifrage (*Saxifraga oppositifolia*), the Roseroot (*Sedum rosea*), the Moss Campion (*Silene acaulis*), the Alpine Meadow Rue (*Thalictrum alpinum*), and the Alpine Speedwell (*Veronica alpina*). Among other interesting plants are the Brook Saxifrage (*Saxifraga rivularis*), the Curved Woodrush (*Luzula arcuata*), the Lesser Twayblade (*Listera cordata*), the Chickweed Wintergreen (*Trientalis europaea*), and the Globeflower (*Trollius europaeus*).

The Cairngorms form one of the most suitable areas for the study of altitudinal limits of plants. The Scots Pine rarely occurs higher than

M

about 2,000 feet as a tree, although seedlings reach 3,400 feet on Ben Macdhui. Birch goes up to 2,300 feet and Common Sallow to 2,400 feet. Common Dandelions have been found up to more than 3,000 feet, common Daisies up to about 2,500 feet, Ling is dominant up to 2,800 feet and Cross-leaved Heath up to 2,300 feet, and the Meadow Buttercup up to 3,800. On the other hand Grass of Parnassus (*Parnassia palustris*) stops at about 2,000 feet and Bog Myrtle (*Myrica gale*) about 1,500 feet, while the Creeping Lady's Tresses (*Goodyera repens*) has a limit of about 1,000 feet, which brings it only into the lowest parts of the Reserve. The impressive Pine wood in Glen Derry containing more than 4,000 trees is nearly all above the 1,400-foot contour. Pine stumps are found in the bogs up to about 2,900 feet.

The extensive open Pine forest of Rothiemurchus interspersed with tall and flourishing Juniper is one of the largest and most impressive relics of the Caledonian Forest, and one of the few which is still regenerating freely.

The Cairngorms Nature Reserve is also outstanding for its birds, including the Golden Eagle, Ptarmigan, Dotterel, Snow Bunting, Blackcock, Greenshank, Crested Tit and Scottish Crossbill. A point of interest ornithologically is that the zone of overlap and hybridisation between the Carrion and Hooded Crows, which used to run well to the south of the Reserve, now runs through it and is apparently still shifting northwards. Hybrids are therefore regularly seen. Among mammals the most conspicuous are the Red Deer, Roe Deer and Mountain Hare. Wild Cats occur only on the lowest fringes. Red Squirrels are still common in Rothiemurchus, although their numbers fluctuate greatly.

While less is known about the invertebrates, a number of investigations have recently been carried out even on the highest summits and some interesting records of insect migration have been obtained. Some insects living on the more exposed tops have developed flightless forms which help in preventing them from being blown away.

Geologically the Cairngorms are a large granite mass rising to a surprisingly uniform summit plateau around 4,000 feet above sea level, deeply intersected by denudation and by the extensive impacts of the Ice Ages which have left many perfect examples of corries, moraines and characteristic U-shaped profiles in the valleys.

The Reserve is wholly uninhabited except for one of the Wardens and his family who live on its fringe. While part of it is owned by the Nature Conservancy, the greater part has been included by Nature Reserve Agreements with Colonel J. P. Grant of Rothiemurchus and with the

54. *Male Snow Bunting.*

55. *Dotterel at its nest.*

56. *Red Deer under the Cairngorms, with mature Scots Pines.*

Mar and Inshriach Estates. The Grants of Rothiemurchus have for several generations been active protectors of wildlife and a medal for his attempts—unfortunately unsuccessful—to protect the Ospreys at Loch-an-Eilein was presented to John Peter Grant of Rothiemurchus as long ago as 1893 by the Zoological Society of London.

Conservation on the Deeside area has an even longer, although very different, history. The Forest of Mar is reputedly the oldest Scottish Deer Forest. In 1584 James VI appointed a Forester and Keeper with special powers to deal with poachers of the Deer and 'Muirfoulis'. Except for intense persecution of predators during the eighteenth and nineteenth centuries, the wildlife attracted by the mountains has on the whole been well cared for, which is why so much of it remains for us to conserve for posterity.

Beinn Eighe, Ross-shire

NATURE CONSERVANCY RESERVE

48 miles west of Inverness and ¼ mile from Kinlochewe: 10,450 acres. ACCESS. *Unrestricted*

UNTIL a few centuries ago most of Scotland except the highest ground was covered with bog and forest. As Scotland is so near the Arctic, and yet washed by the Gulf Stream, several distinct forest types were represented including Birchwoods in the north-west, dense Hazel scrub with scattered Oak and Ash in the Inner Hebrides and elsewhere, Juniper scrub at medium altitudes in the Highlands with Birch, Rowan and Alder on the richer soils, Oak at low altitudes in the south and west, and the great Caledonian forest dominated by Pine in the heart of the Highlands.

Ruthless over-burning and over-grazing by successive generations have so destroyed and degraded these forests that only the most pains-taking research in the surviving remnants can show what they were like and how, by working with nature, part at least of the Highlands may be restored to health and freed from the curses of erosion, soil impoverishment and the spread of Bracken and other consequences of wrong land use and mistaken land management.

At the south-east of Loch Maree in the North-West Highlands there still survives a badly damaged relic of the western type of the Caledonian Pine forest spread over about 600 acres of the 10,000-acre Beinn Eighe

Nature Reserve. Loch Maree is near enough to the Atlantic to have a strongly oceanic climate and is at the meeting place of several different woodland types. Here at the Anancaun Field Station is centred the Nature Conservancy's research into the composition and ecology of the great Caledonian Forest. This western variant of Scottish Pine woods differs from the typical development along Deeside and Strathspey in the abundance of other tree species such as Oak, Holly, Rowan and Birch, the rarity of Juniper and the luxuriance of Sphagnum and other mosses on the forest floor.

Deer and straying livestock have been excluded by fencing from a 100 acre plot and experiments in progress are mainly concerned with the natural regeneration of Pine in various vegetation types and methods of afforestation by direct seed sowing. The extent and the fate of an earlier and more widespread forest have been traced from a well-marked layer of Pine charcoal between the peat and the underlying sands and gravels, which confirms local legends of an early forest having been destroyed by fire.

Anancaun is also the scene of the most extensive programme of climatological observations in the North-West Highlands. These are helping to explain the significant differences between West Highland and East Highland weather. Another familiar curse of the Highlands has been investigated by the Midge Control Unit from Edinburgh University, using Anancaun Field Station as an advanced base.

Most of the Reserve is on Cambrian quartzite and Pre-Cambrian Torridon Sandstone, the soil and vegetation of which are remarkably poor. Contrasting with these are patches of soil, developed from Cambrian dolomite and shale, carrying a varied vegetation which has been studied in much detail. The Kinlochewe Thrust and the results of glaciation add to the geological interest. A reconnaissance soil survey and examination of sample soil profiles have been undertaken by the Macaulay Institute for Soil Research. A series of detailed entomological investigations have been made by entomologists from London, Oxford and elsewhere and a collection has been formed of 'Voucher Specimens' identified by specialists and available for comparison.

This is particularly necessary as no other site in the North-West Highlands has been so intensively studied as Beinn Eighe and many species encountered are either new or little known in the region. On the other hand, as the invertebrate fauna is much more limited than in southern Britain, the task of studying it as a whole is more manageable though still intensely complex. Special attention has been given to invertebrates which may play a part in aiding or hindering tree regeneration. Fungi, lichens and bryophytes have also been specially investigated since the establishment of this, the first British National Nature Reserve, in November, 1951.

The mammals of the Reserve include the Wild Cat and Pine Marten which, although constantly present, are rarely seen, and then most often along the main road leading past the Reserve along the shores of Loch Maree. The Red Deer and the Mountain Hare are also among the characteristic mammals, while the birds include Ptarmigan and sometimes Golden Eagles on the higher ground, and Redstart, Whinchat, Wood Warbler, Redpoll and Bullfinch in the wood. Black-throated Divers breed on the adjoining Loch and the Grasshopper Warbler, a very rare bird in the North-West Highlands, has been recorded on the Conservancy's farm land just outside the Reserve. During the great Crossbill invasion of Britain in June, 1953, Crossbills reached this remote wood by June 14, four days after their first appearance in North Sutherland, and before their arrival in Orkney, Shetland and other areas along the North Sea coast nearer to their point of departure in Scandinavia.

Although still in its earliest years, the scientific work at Beinn Eighe has already demonstrated how many important possibilities it holds and how little we yet know scientifically about the Highlands in spite of the vast amount which has been written about them.

North Rona and Sula Sgeir, Ross-shire

NATURE CONSERVANCY RESERVE

Some 47 miles north-west of Cape Wrath: 320 acres. Under Nature Reserve Agreement with the owners, the Barvas Estate.
ACCESS. *Unrestricted*

INACCESSIBLE and uninhabited islands make good Nature Reserves. There is little competition over them unless they are unfortunate enough to become involved in some Defence project, while the difficulty and expense of the voyage and the landing often in bad weather on a poor landing place is a strong deterrent to excessive disturbance. On the other hand, there are peculiar difficulties about managing Nature Reserve which at any given time it is impossible to be sure of getting on or, having got on, of getting off again.

Personally, although I have circled low over North Rona in a flying boat and have sailed close under its cliffs, I have never had an opportunity to land on it. This is disappointing as it is the most important of all nurseries of the Atlantic Grey Seal, and Dr Fraser Darling, when he spent the period November-December, 1938, on the island during the seals' breeding season, estimated that he saw 5,000 ashore there and that this was probably at the time about half the entire world population of the species.

Prior to 1890 it was estimated that between 120 and 150 Grey Seals were killed annually on North Rona. Up to 1844 the island was inhabited and it seems likely that the present population of seals is higher than it has been for a very long time. The aerial survey of September, 1947, indicated that over 1,000 calves a year are produced on North Rona. It was astonishing to see the seals lying about thickly, not only on the rocks by the sea but right up the hillside which was plainly marked where they had dragged their bodies over the vegetation.

North Rona is also the home of one of the few British colonies of Leach's Petrel, which breeds mainly on the western shores of the Atlantic down to Maine. Mr John A. Ainslie and Mr Robert Atkinson, who studied this colony, say: 'It is evident that this species is the most oceanic in habit of all British breeding birds and, at its nesting haunts, the most inaccessible. This, coupled with the facts that the bird is on land entirely nocturnal and nests underground, easily explains why it has been so little studied.' In 1939 they spent a night on Sula Sgeir, a rock covering a mere 20 acres some 10 miles west of North Rona, and estimated that the colony of Leach's Petrels there probably amounted to some 400 pairs or about as many as on North Rona. Recent reports indicate much reduced numbers.

Sula Sgeir also has an important Gannetry, which contained 4,500 breeding pairs in 1937, and is the subject of a special order by the Secretary of State for Scotland, legalising the recognised traditional annual harvest of young Gannets by the men of Ness, near the Butt of Lewis, subject to a close season being observed from February 1 to August 31.

North Rona extends over 300 acres and is 47 miles north-west of Cape Wrath and about as far from the Butt of Lewis. Its ridge rises to 355 feet and is composed of Lewisian gneiss, one of the earliest geological formations. Archaeologically St Ronan's Cell is interesting as possibly the oldest Christian building in Britain still to be seen in its original state.

57. *Beinn Eighe Nature Reserve. Coille na Glas-Leitire, Scots Pine and Birch Wood, Loch Maree, still a Pine Marten habitat.*

58. *Pine Marten.*

Noss, Shetland

NATURE CONSERVANCY RESERVE

774 acres. Established under Nature Reserve Agreement with Mr Norman Cameron of Garth: wardened by Royal Society for the Protection of Birds. ACCESS. *Intending visitors should contact Messrs. G. and L. Sutherland, Noss*

Noss is an island of Old Red Sandstone covering 774 acres and rising at the Noup sheer out of the sea for almost 600 feet. It is only three miles from Lerwick, the capital of Shetland, and is separated from Bressay by a channel only 200 yards broad from which a rough moorland grazed by sheep slopes gradually up to the summit. Although now only inhabited in summer, Noss used to have a chapel and burial ground and parts of it were cultivated by two or three families a couple of centuries ago.

The breeding birds include the Twite, Wheatear, Peregrine, Eider, Rock Dove, Arctic Tern, Black Guillemot and a number of spectacular colonial nesting species, including immense numbers of Kittiwakes whose most important flight-line has been estimated to be used by 40,000-50,000 daily at the height of the breeding season. Puffins are described by the Venables as nesting here in 'extremely high numbers' and Guillemots as having a strength of 'many thousand pairs'. The outward stream of Guillemots from the colony during the breeding season has been estimated at more than 90,000 birds daily, although in recent years a steady decline has occurred, as Gannets take over their nesting ledges. Razorbills are not nearly so numerous and their numbers have been estimated at fewer than 1,000 pairs, while the numbers of Fulmars are considerably higher. The first pair of Gannets bred in 1914 and numbers rose to over 1,500 by 1938 and to more than 2,000 by 1949. A less appreciated colony is that of about 150 pairs of Great Black-backed Gulls on the flat top of the Holm of Noss, forming the largest concentration of these big and destructive birds in Shetland.

The main feature of Noss is its possession of one of the most spectacular cliff breeding colonies in Britain, not unduly difficult of access and extensively used in scientific investigations. Away from the cliffs the most important colonial breeding species is the Great Skua or Bonxie which, as at Hermaness, has greatly increased and was credited with about 165 pairs in 1952. It is believed to do considerable damage among the other sea birds.

Several species are known to have become extinct on Noss, including the Corn Bunting, Skylark, Cormorant, Curlew, Golden Plover and two particularly unfortunate losses—the Whimbrel (which still breeds elsewhere in Shetland) and the White-tailed or Sea Eagle. The male of the pair which used to nest here was killed in 1908, but his mate continued sitting on her nest annually until 1918, the last of the British Sea Eagles. Under strict protection the Sea Eagle has returned to Denmark, where it had also been exterminated. We can never abandon hope that some day it may also return here, aided by a more sensible and less repressive attitude towards birds of prey.

The Nature Reserve was established in 1955 by a Nature Reserve Agreement with the proprietor.

Hermaness, Shetland

NATURE CONSERVANCY RESERVE

In north-west of island of Unst: 1,071 acres. Under Nature Reserve Agreement with Lt. Col. Laurence Edmondston. Wardened by Royal Society for the Protection of Birds. ACCESS. Intending visitors should contact L. Bruce, Bothen, Haroldswick, Lerwick

MUCKLE FLUGGA and its Out Stack, which are within the Hermaness Nature Reserve, are the most northerly of the British Isles, reaching within eight minutes of the sixty-first Parallel, and just overlapping Southern Greenland which extends a little farther south.

Muckle Flugga has the larger of the two Shetland colonies of Gannets. Gannets have bred in Shetland only since about 40 years ago, although their bones are freely found in prehistoric settlements and they have always been frequent offshore. The colony must have been heavily reinforced from outside, since it grew to about 1,000 pairs by 1935 and to over 2,600 by 1939. It has probably continued to grow since, but the difficulty of approach and the large numbers of non-breeders sitting on the nesting cliffs, together with bad weather conditions, have frustrated attempts at more recent checks. The birds return to Muckle Flugga annually with the herrings early in February and many remain until October, when the flightless young are already swimming southwards until their wings become strong enough to carry them down to their winter quarters off Spain and North Africa. Most of the Reserve is a peninsula on the north-west of the island of Unst,

59. *Hermaness Nature Reserve, Shetland. Cliffs with Muckle Flugga Light house, Britain's most northerly outpost, in the distance.*

60. *Smooth Snake (Coronella austriaca).*

61. Hales Wood Nature Reserve. Oak-Ash standards with coppice, forming Oxlip habitat.

on to which much of the gannetry has overflowed, this being the only example on the European side of the Atlantic of a gannetry on a large inhabited island.

The cliffs of the Hermaness Reserve are also notable for their great numbers of nesting Fulmars. Breeding began here about 1897, some 20 years after the expansion from the original British breeding colony at St Kilda had started with the occupation of Foula. The strength of the colony was estimated at about 2,000 pairs in 1949, which would make it about the seventh most important Fulmar colony in the British Isles.

Neither the Gannet nor the Fulmar, however, has played so important a part in the history of Hermaness as another bird, the Great Skua. This powerful, piratical sea-bird lives largely on fish disgorged by frightened gulls and other victims, often after an exciting chase. It is found both in Antarctic and North Atlantic waters, but not in the North Pacific, and has no breeding stations on the continent of Europe. In the nineteenth century the Bonxie, as it is called in Shetland, was so severely persecuted that its total extinction seemed almost inevitable. About 70 years ago Hermaness was probably the only place, except Foula, where the species survived, and there were not more than half a dozen pairs. Numbers began to rise at the end of the century and they had increased to at least 80 pairs by 1922 and to at least 300 pairs, by no means all breeding, in 1949. This represented somewhere about a third of the entire British population of the species.

The survival of the species here is due in the first place to Dr L. Edmondston, who intervened when the numbers had been reduced to three pairs as long ago as 1831. He built up the population gradually to 50 or 60 pairs. In 1891 a successor, Mr T. Edmondston, put a keeper on Hermaness to look after the birds and subsequently the burden of maintaining a watcher was assumed by the Royal Society for the Protection of Birds. It is an interesting illustration of the continuity and spirit of co-operation in nature conservation that the present owner, Lt.-Col. Laurence Edmondston, has made an agreement with the Nature Conservancy which affords Crown Land status for the Reserve, although he continues as proprietor and the Royal Society for the Protection of Birds continues to provide a Warden.

In the breeding season wardening is effectively helped by the Bonxies which swoop repeatedly at the heads of visitors crossing their ground and occasionally succeed in knocking off hats and inflicting blows. Arctic Skuas, a smaller species, have decreased recently, owing possibly to being preyed upon by their larger relatives. The Bonxies leave be-

N

tween September and March and one ringed at Hermaness on July 3, 1939, was recovered on the Massachusetts coast the following February.

One of the greatest losses has been the extinction as a breeding species of the White-tailed Eagle, which ceased to breed at Hermaness a century ago, although one was seen flying high overhead as recently as 1949.

The peninsula consists of gneiss largely covered with rough moorland and blanket bog and dotted with many lochans.

Rhum, Inner Hebrides

NATURE CONSERVANCY RESERVE

10 *miles west of Mallaig:* 26,400 *acres.* ACCESS. *Permits required except for head of Loch Scresort*

RHUM is much smaller than its northern neighbour, Skye, and belongs to the Parish of the Small Isles. Being about 8 miles in both breadth and depth, it is, however, the second largest of Britain's Nature Reserves, and the largest wholly owned by the Nature Conservancy, who bought it in 1957 from the Trustees of the late Sir George Bullough.

Rhum is the product of intense volcanic action, which has given it a remarkable mountain skyline dominated by Askival (2,659 feet) and other mountains, which gain in impressiveness as they rise within a mile or two of the sea and within sight of the Skye Cuillins and other famous peaks. The geology is of great interest and complexity, with Torridonian sandstone giving place to ultra-basic rocks, including allivalite, named after Hallival, Askival's neighbour. The interpretation of the geological events is still in dispute.

Rhum is noted for its rare plants, including *Thlaspi alpestre*, and for its mammals, including two island races, the Rhum Mouse (*Apodemus hebridensis hamiltoni*) and the Hebridean Vole (*Microtus agrestis exsul*). The most conspicuous mammals are, however, the large herd of Red Deer and the Grey Seals. Among birds Rhum has its quota of Golden Eagles and a unique mountain-top breeding colony of Manx Shearwaters, some nesting well over 2,000 feet. Non-scientific visitors are often most impressed with the numbers and viciousness of the horseflies or clegs, the midges and the sheep-ticks.

The main object of the Nature Reserve is scientific work on the enrichment of mountain and moorland vegetation by scientific management, particularly as regards grazing pressures and burning; full investigation of Red Deer problems with the aid of the self-contained herd; study of the food of Golden Eagles; and experiments in the provision of windbreaks and in restoring tree cover. The island is particularly fitted for such purposes as it has a long history of freedom from disturbance and exploitation, and is ideally suited for scientific investigations requiring complete quiet and immunity from interference.

St Kilda, Outer Hebrides

NATURE CONSERVANCY RESERVE

A property of the National Trust for Scotland. 45 miles west of the Outer Hebrides: 2,107 acres. ACCESS. *Unrestricted*

WHILE some British Nature Reserves represent no more than a fragment or a worn relic of their former grandeur, St Kilda is by any standards a great nature monument. No other sea cliffs in Great Britain rise so high sheer out of the ocean. Conachair on Hirta stands up over a quarter of a mile above the waves, while two other islands of the group, Boreray and Soay, are both over 1,200 feet. Stac an Armin, a mere isolated rock pinnacle in form, is half as high again as the spire of Salisbury Cathedral.

Having escaped burial under the great British ice-cap during successive glaciations, St Kilda is equally impressive for the antiquity of its flora and fauna. It has probably been one of the North Atlantic's greatest sea-bird colonies continuously since long before the time when the ice covered Britain down to about Golders Green and Clifton. It has lost much (and saddest of all the Great Auk during last century), but it still possesses its unique bird, the St Kilda Wren, its unique native mammal, the St Kilda long-tailed field mouse, and its peculiar ancestral race of sheep, the Soay sheep, which now lives wild as indeed do the Blackfaces on Boreray, unshepherded since the St Kildans were evacuated at their own request by the Government in 1930. Several colonies are now known of Leach's Petrel, a fork-tailed species rare on this side of the Atlantic.

St Kilda is famous for its immense and very ancient colony of Fulmars, larger petrels on which the inhabitants mainly depended for meat, oil and feathers. The Gannets also have here their largest colony in the world, which had about 17,000 pairs in 1939 and now has even more. But the most numerous by far of St Kilda's nesting birds is the Puffin, whose numbers have hitherto defied attempts at census, but certainly run well into six figures and perhaps even to seven.

St Kilda is perhaps the most exciting to the imagination of all British nature reserves, whether it is first seen from a small boat under sail (the best introduction) or from an aircraft. It was unfortunate that the necessities of the Hebridean Guided Missile Range should have led to its quiet and solitude being broken by the construction of manned radar stations, but by close co-operation between the Services, the National Trust for Scotland (who are the new owners) and the Nature Conservancy (who will manage it as a nature reserve) it is hoped to minimise such damage as cannot be averted and to maintain the essential character and scientific interest of the islands. Access across these stormy waters must unfortunately remain discouragingly difficult for any but the really keen, and for those sent there under military discipline.

Other Nature Reserves

* Access restricted
† Access partly restricted
‡ Access unrestricted

B RIEF descriptions have been given separately for 46 of the most important and most characteristic Nature Reserves at present existing in Great Britain, but this is far from being the whole story of Britain's Nature Reserves, for others are in process of negotiation. In addition there are many other Nature Reserves, or areas which are so owned or managed that they have a claim to be considered in this connection. To have attempted to describe them all separately would have forced up the size and price of this book far beyond desirable limits or would have reduced the separate descriptions of the more important ones to even briefer thumbnail sketches than they already must be.

In this concluding section, therefore, the other Nature Reserves which it has not been possible to mention separately will be very summarily reviewed, in most cases receiving little more than mere mention, which is far less than a number of them deserve. Many of them, however, have more or less close affinities with types that have been described more fully, and it is hoped that the reader who bears this in mind will be able to gain some idea of their significance.

Beginning with the Isles of Scilly, the small island called Annet* has long been kept quiet as a bird sanctuary by the care of the Dorrien-Smith family and with the friendly informality which is such a pleasant feature of the Scillies. The large colony of Manx Shearwaters is the outstanding feature of Annet, which is also known for its small breeding colony of Roseate Terns.

Near the Furzebrook Research Station of the Nature Conservancy south of Wareham in Dorset, the Nature Conservancy have two small Nature Reserves, one at Arne* consisting of a piece of oak woodland running down immediately to salt marsh, rather like the edge of Roudsea Wood, and the other consisting of a small bog known as Hartland Moor,* which is interesting as being possibly the best locality for the rare Dorset Heath (*Erica ciliaris*). It is also the scene of important researches on populations of both vegetarian and animal-eating ants. A few miles northward is the Conservancy's important Morden Bog Nature Reserve,* which contains ants and other invertebrates of otherwise south European distribution.

Ham Street Woods,* in Kent, overlook Romney Marsh and were on the south coast before the changes, which led to the formation of Dungeness in quite recent times, completely altered the coastline. These rich and varied woodlands became a National Nature Reserve in 1952. They form a good example of the coppice-with-standards type of woodland once so familiar in south-east England and now rapidly degenerating or disappearing. They also contain some interesting plants and are particularly important as a haunt of rare insects otherwise found only on the Continent.

Blean Woods,* also in Kent near Canterbury, have suffered serious devastation from timber cutting. The Conservancy's Reserve area is particularly interesting as a centre of the last remaining native haunt of the Heath Fritillary, an attractive species of butterfly.

Swanscombe Skull Site† is a peculiar Nature Reserve now closely ringed by modern housing, but of international importance as the site of the discovery in 1935-6 of the Swanscombe Skull, the brain case of a human being of the period of the Acheulian hand-axe makers, dating from at least 100,000 years ago. The value of preserving this site was emphasised in July, 1955, when Mr John Wymer and his colleagues discovered further important fragments of the skull while digging under licence from the Nature Conservancy.

Belfairs Great Wood,‡ owned by the Southend Borough Council, was bought with the assistance of the Society for the Promotion of Nature Reserves and is one of the best examples of urban Nature Reserves in Britain. All three Woodpeckers and also the Tawny Owl and Sparrow Hawk bred in it successfully in 1954, and in addition to the introduced Heath Fritillary and the High Brown Fritillary, the White Admiral and also the Purple Hairstreak still occur. A large number of schoolchildren undertake field studies in the wood.

Hales Wood* in Essex is one of the rare examples of a Conservancy Nature Reserve which exists primarily to preserve a single species—the true Oxlip (*Primula elatior*), which grows only in a small area where Essex, Suffolk and Cambridgeshire meet.

High Standing Hill,* in Windsor Forest, is a small 'Wilderness Area' set aside and kept quiet by the Crown Estate Commissioners. It is covered largely by Beech and Oak growing much as they have done here since at least Norman times. This is very rich entomologically and has been studied by entomologists from the neighbouring Silwood Park Field Station of Imperial College, London.

Cothill Nature Reserve,* Berkshire, at present includes only the small Ruskin Reserve, which has already been protected since 1917 by the National Trust in co-operation with the Ashmolean Natural History Society. It is a small and rather dangerous fen, including two ponds and various swamp associations of Alder, Birch, Ash and other trees.

As the Forestry Commission controls such large areas of woodland in Great Britain, the thought has naturally occurred to them and to the Nature Conservancy that certain conservation needs might most suitably be met by the Commission setting aside limited areas in the forests under their management on which conservation and ecological research might be practised. Agreement was reached in 1954 on the management of nearly 200 acres of Waterperry Wood* near Oxford in the interests of nature conservation and ecological research jointly with those of timber production. The insect fauna of this wood is particularly rich and is studied by scientists from Oxford University. This informal arrangement between the two Crown bodies concerned will be watched with interest by the naturalists and research workers affected.

Mickfield Meadow,† in Suffolk, is a very small area which was acquired by the Society for the Promotion of Nature Reserves primarily with the object of conserving that rare and attractive flower, the Fritillary (*Fritillaria meleagris*). As this plant flourishes under grazing and by the control of woody vegetation, the correct management of the Reserve is similar to that of neighbouring pasture, but with the addition of effective control of plucking and uprooting of plants. Some difficulties have arisen about managing it on these lines, but it is thought that they have now been overcome.

North Warren,* near Aldeburgh in east Suffolk, is a small Royal Society for the Protection of Birds Reserve of about 130 acres of heath and bracken sloping down to a reedy fen, where Bitterns, Garganey, Grasshopper Warblers, Red-backed Shrikes, Woodlarks and Stonechats are among the birds observed in the breeding season, as well as Stone Curlews. One of the most serious problems on this Reserve has been the frequency of fires started by passing trains, and the recent conversion of the passenger service to diesel will, it is hoped, reduce this evil. The Wryneck, now a very rare bird, has bred lately in this area.

Westleton Heath,* in Suffolk, is a small Reserve belonging to the Nature Conservancy adjoining the larger Minsmere Bird Reserve. It is chiefly known for its birds, including the Stone Curlew, Stonechat, Woodlark and Red-backed Shrike. It is, however, one of the few good surviving examples of the formerly extensive heathlands of east Suffolk.

Cavenham Heath,‡ in west Suffolk, has suffered gravely in recent years from agricultural reclamation and the encroachment of a large airfield. It is, however, still probably the best example of the sequence from dry, acid, sandy heath and shallow basic soils typical of Breckland, to reed and sedge and peat and damp willow carr along the river Lark, with a rich and varied flora and fauna. The small existing Reserve is only a fragment of the Conservancy's proposed eventual Reserve area.

Thetford Heath,* just within the Suffolk boundary about two miles south-west of Thetford, was prudently secured by the Norfolk Naturalists Trust in order to safeguard its wild life and to avert its development. In addition to the typical Breckland birds, it is interesting geologically as showing some strange stone stripes which are attributed to solifluction due to glacial action. The sudden vanishing of rabbits through myxomatosis has allowed the herbage to spring up to an unaccustomed height, greatly changing the appearance of the heath and embarrassing such birds as Wheatears which depend on open ground and on well-maintained rabbit burrows.

Surlingham and Rockland Broads,† lying south of the Yare, are much more strongly tidal than the Bure Broads and show large stretches of Reed Grass (*Glyceria maxima*), some of which occur as the floating hover-fen peculiar to the Yare Valley. Much of the fen has grown up to a swampy wooded carr, which could easily pass muster in a film about some unexplored tropical jungle. Coypus have been very active here in adding to the extent of open water. The area has been worked by botanists and zoologists with great success in recent years and is preserved by the Norfolk Naturalists Trust.

Ranworth and Cockshoot Broads,* on the Bure, are managed by the Norfolk Naturalists Trust primarily as a duck sanctuary. Some of the recent studies which have greatly changed scientific opinion on the origin of the Norfolk Broads have been done in this area.

Barton Broad,† preserved by the Norfolk Naturalists Trust, includes the best unspoilt swamp Alderwood in the region and many interesting aquatic habitats showing a particularly rich insect fauna. In no other part of Britain has the conservation of so many ecologically important areas been assured entirely by local initiative and enterprise.

Winterton Dunes* is the largest mainland dune system on the East Anglian coast, having a maximum width of 600 yards and providing exceptionally interesting contrasts with the calcareous west coast dunes. The northern part was declared by the Conservancy as a National Nature Reserve in September, 1956, but the southern part, which also includes botanical and physiographical features of the highest interest, had to be omitted owing to the ill-advised development which occurred here before the Second World War.

Blakeney Point,‡ in north Norfolk, is the culmination of a particularly interesting stretch of coast, also including Salthouse Broad and the intermediate marshes at Cley. The last named are owned by the Norfolk Naturalists Trust and Blakeney Point by the National Trust. Blakeney has historic significance as the first Nature Reserve to be established in Norfolk, having been acquired in 1912, mainly through the efforts of Professor F. W. Oliver of University College, London, who carried out much research here even before the First World War and expressed satisfaction 'that so wonderful a collection of natural habitats should have been secured by the wise generosity of the donors against the possibility of any interference with the operation of natural factors'. Unfortunately, subsequent pressure of population and especially of summer visitors has made the realisation of this hope difficult and precarious and has given evidence that only enlightened and vigilant public opinion can prevent the gradual deterioration or destruction even of areas which are specifically acquired as Nature Reserves. Although much important scientific work has been done at Blakeney, the recent trend has been towards greater reliance on Scolt Head Island which is not subject to quite so much disturbance by visitors.

62. Wren's Nest Nature Reserve. Caverns under the 'Seven Sisters' facing north on west flank.

63. *St Kilda Nature Reserve. Village Bay, Hirta, showing Manse in centre and stone ' cleits ' on Oiseval (left) with Dun behind R.A.F.V.* Bridport.

64. *Cliffs on St Kilda between Oiseval and Conachair, showing Puffin slopes.*

65. *Flying Fulmars with distant gannetry on Stac an Armin (left), Stac Lee and Boreray from Hirta.*

Castor Hanglands,† near Peterborough, is a Conservancy Nature Reserve particularly important for its insect life. It consists of mixed woodland, heath and grassland on Oolitic limestone and calcareous clays, and forms part of the Nene group of Nature Reserves together with Holme Fen, Woodwalton Fen and Monks' Wood.

The New Grounds,* at Slimbridge between the river Severn and the Gloucester and Berkeley Canal, have recently been developed as probably the most famous wildfowl reserve in Europe and an international centre of wildfowl research. Of the 243 living forms of Anatidae known to science, 149 have been kept in the collection at one time or another, including something like one third of the surviving world population of Hawaiian Geese. During the winter of 1953-4 as many as nine species and sub-species of geese reached the New Grounds in a wild state, including a Red-breasted Goose and four Lesser White-fronted Geese, for which the New Grounds form the only fairly regular wintering station in Britain. The majority of the wintering geese are of the European White-fronted species, whose numbers sometimes rise to as many as 5,000. With its headquarters at this remote spot, the Wildfowl Trust has in nine years built up a membership of some 5,000 and an annual income of about £40,000. More than 100,000 people visit the New Grounds annually and although many of them watch the wild geese from observation posts, they do so without disturbing the birds which continue to come back in undiminished numbers every season.

Wren's Nest,‡ in Worcestershire, is exclusively a geological Reserve on which important geological work has been done for many generations. It is the first Nature Reserve created by agreement between the Nature Conservancy and an important municipality.

Dovedale Ashwood‡ is a small part of the National Trust properties in the picturesque valley of the river Dove, about four miles north-north-west of Ashbourne, on which little planting or selective felling has taken place for centuries, because the steep gullies and spurs are extremely difficult of access. Mixed with the Ashwood are Oak, Beech, Wych Elm, Sycamore and Birch of all ages, regenerating freely with a varied shrub layer including Holly, Yew and Honeysuckle and an interesting ground flora. By informal agreement with ecologists, the National Trust are taking steps to preserve the high scientific interest of this remnant of the natural woodlands.

Another valuable remnant—this time of sessile Oak woodland—has survived for similar reasons in the Conservancy's National Nature Reserve in the gorge of the river Rheidol,* just above Devil's Bridge near

o

Aberystwyth. Here the rainfall is about 60 inches annually and the humidity is so high that the fauna and flora resemble those of the Killarney woods in western Ireland. In primitive times such woodlands were no doubt quite widely distributed in Wales.

In 1956 the Lincolnshire Naturalists' Trust succeeded in obtaining from the Air Ministry a lease of nearly 170 acres of sand dunes at Saltfleetby and Theddlethorpe,‡ including some old grass dunes with Sea Buckthorn and Elder scrub and an extensive freshwater slack harbouring many plants and animals rare or absent from other parts of Lincolnshire. This scientifically interesting area had recently been used as a rubbish dump, which in addition to its unsightliness had attracted rats. It will be a valuable complement to Gibraltar Point both for conservation and research.

The interesting heathlands of north Lincolnshire have recently been very heavily damaged or destroyed by iron-ore operations, afforestation and reclamation. The Lincolnshire Naturalists' Trust in 1954 acquired a small area at Scotton Common* and arranged for a vegetation survey to be made of it, and a management scheme to be put in hand. The object is to maintain the existing variety of habitats with their characteristic flora and fauna and to re-create types of habitat which have almost or entirely disappeared. Financial assistance for this purpose has been given by the Society for the Promotion of Nature Reserves.

Wybunbury Moss,* in south Cheshire, is an unusually large example of a 'schwingmoor', a type of bog exceptional in Britain. Its centre is covered by a thin crust of Sphagnum peat six to ten feet deep, floating on water, while the vegetation round the margin is a fen community. Access to this Conservancy Reserve is hazardous and it is not open to the public.

Marbury Reed Bed,* in Cheshire, is managed by the Society for the Promotion of Nature Reserves. Although a small area it is attractive to birds as long as it can be kept quiet, and is one of the most northern localities in England for the breeding of Reed Warblers.

Askham Bog,* near York, managed by the Yorkshire Naturalists' Trust, is the remnant of a much more extensive swamp, most of which has been reclaimed for agriculture. It is well known to entomologists as a stronghold of many species which are rare or becoming extinct elsewhere and its plants include the Grass of Parnassus and the Royal and Marsh Ferns. Much of it has grown up to Alder and Willow carr, with some Alder Buckthorn (*Frangula alnus*).

Castle Eden Denes,‡ in County Durham, form the only example still worth preserving of the steep-sided wooded denes which run down to the coast in this region and which were so attractive before the development of coal mining. The Reserve contains a number of rare plants and insects and is geologically interesting. It was declared in December, 1954, on the basis of a Nature Reserve Agreement between the Durham County Council, the Easington Rural District Council and the Peterlee Development Corporation, being the only instance of a Statutory Nature Reserve established in a New Town.

Blelham Bog,‡ on Blelham Tarn, and North Fen,‡ on Esthwaite Water, are very small Conservancy Reserves in the Lake District National Park in North Lancashire which have been considerably studied by biologists from the Freshwater Biological Association's station on Windermere. North Fen is interesting as illustrating the vegetational succession from open water rich in mineral salts through fen to fen carr and bog, while Blelham Bog is a rare example of Sphagnum bog developing from wet woodland, whose presence below the surface peat has been demonstrated by boring.

Meathop Moss,† in Westmorland, was made a Nature Reserve by the Society for the Promotion of Nature Reserves with the object of preserving a typical Morecambe Bay moss. Unfortunately, the area has deteriorated badly, partly through drainage and drying out and partly through fires and the spread of self-sown trees. The gullery, which existed at the time when it was created, was destroyed by wartime collecting. While it is hoped that the interest of the Reserve may eventually be restored, the history of this area since 1914 illustrates the pitfalls of Nature Reserve management.

Silverflowe‡ is one of the most inaccessible and inhospitable Nature Reserves in Great Britain. It lies in a wild and bleak glen, picturesquely called the Cauldron of the Dungeon in Kirkcudbright, through which a stream called the Cooran Lane meanders lazily with a fall of only 50 feet in two and a half miles. Here has grown up a series of raised bogs which are in a completely natural state and are actively growing. By arrangement with the Forestry Commission, the Nature Conservancy declared the Silverflowe as a Nature Reserve in 1956. It is the only Nature Reserve within the limits of a National Forest Park.

Gleann Diomhan,† in the Isle of Arran, is another example of the precarious survival of interesting native trees only in the steepest and most inaccessible places. Three miles south of Loch Ranza, on ledges of granite and schist on the steep sides of the glen, Dwarf Juniper and Burnet Rose mingle with the two Whitebeam confined to this area of

Arran (*Sorbus arranensis* and *Sorbus pseudofennica*). These trees are scientifically interesting as being the only ones of the dozen or so endemic to Great Britain in this genus, which are found on rock other than limestone. They have been exposed to damage by moor fires and grazing and the Nature Conservancy's Reserve will give them special protection.

Rassal Ashwood† is a rather similar remnant found on a small outcrop of Durness limestone near the head of Loch Kishorn in Wester Ross, where some 30 acres of natural Ashwood survive on the weathered slopes which have become covered with soil and turf to form closely packed hummocks, among which the trees grow mingling with Oaks, Blackthorn and Hazel. This Conservancy Reserve is the most northerly Ashwood in Great Britain. Farther north on the same formation in western Sutherland is the Conservancy's new National Nature Reserve of Inchnadamph,† remarkable for its mixture of limestone ridges and peat-covered hollows, partly clothed in Willow scrub of a type common in Scandinavia, but hitherto undescribed in Scotland.

In writing of Nature Reserves in other countries, it would be necessary to give great prominence to the part played by National Parks. In case anyone should be puzzled by this omission here, it should be recorded that the National Parks which exist in England and Wales— there are none in Scotland—are in practice primarily areas where new development is controlled and, unlike National Parks in most other countries, they are neither owned nor managed by any public authority, nor is it possible to take any steps within them which, so far as the fauna and flora are concerned, differentiate them in any way from other parts of the country. Nature Reserves are created where appropriate, either inside or outside National Parks without distinction.

A number of National Forest Parks are also designated by the Forestry Commission, but here again no special provision is made concerning the fauna and flora. It should, however, always be borne in mind that many both publicly and privately owned estates which are in no ordinary sense Nature Reserves are so managed as to give considerable protection to their wild life, and this applies particularly to the several hundred Sites of Special Scientific Interest which have been notified to owners, occupiers and Local Planning Authorities by the Nature Conservancy, under Section 23 of the National Parks and Access to the Countryside Act.

CONCLUSION

THIS book has outlined the objects, scope and management of Nature Reserves and given brief descriptions of a number. What emerges from it all? Perhaps three points are worth making in conclusion:

(a) There is more in Nature Reserves than meets the eye. They are astonishingly complex, rich, and at the same time precarious. They challenge us to unravel their complexities, to enjoy their riches and to protect them against injury, or deterioration.

(b) Nature Reserves in Britain are mainly very young and are still only fragments of a complete national series. The stage has, however, just been reached when the shape of a balanced series of samples of all the main habitats can be seen emerging, not from any single centralised control, but by the free co-operation of many public and voluntary bodies and private persons, encouraged and assisted by the Nature Conservancy on behalf of the Crown.

(c) The immense range of scientific problems which it becomes possible to study with the aid of Nature Reserves now begins to be discernible. Hundreds of research projects (mostly small) are already in progress on Nature Reserves, yet we have hardly scratched the surface of their potentialities, which stretch many decades into the future. These include not only fundamental problems of ecology, but applied problems of erosion, coast defence, land use, land management, water conservation, the growing of trees and the grazing of animals. The obstacles which have hitherto held back science at these points have now largely been removed, and Nature Reserves may well in future be regarded as fully justifying their existence by their contribution as outdoor laboratories alone. No doubt, however, the ordinary man and woman will look on them first as places simply to enjoy and perhaps sometimes to be thankful for. Our aim must be, patiently but firmly, to hold our Nature Reserves in trust for both, but above all for the animals and plants which have nowhere else to go.

REMINDER

This seems the appropriate point to remind readers that while a number of these Nature Reserves are freely open to visitors, many others are either private property or have to be restricted for the protection of their wild life or of delicate scientific work in progress. In most cases collecting of specimens is not permitted on Nature Reserves. Much embarrassment and difficulty is caused by enthusiastic, but inconsiderate, people who neglect to take the proper steps when they wish to see a Reserve, access to which has to be restricted. One of the objects of this book is to ensure that anyone interested can readily find out which Reserves can be visited without formality, and in other cases whom to approach for permission to visit them. Please do your best by complying to help our wild life and those who have responsibility for its welfare and study.

ABRIDGED BIBLIOGRAPHY

GENERAL

Ministry of Town and Country Planning (1947), *Conservation of Nature in England and Wales. Report of the Wild Life Conservation Special Committee (England and Wales)*. Cmd. 7122. H.M. Stationery Office.

Department of Health for Scotland (1949), *Nature Reserves in Scotland. Final Report by the Scottish National Parks Committee and the Scottish Wild Life Conservation Committee*. Cmd. 7814. H.M. Stationery Office.

National Parks and Access to the Countryside Act, 1949, 12, 13 & 14 Geo. 6, Ch. 97. H.M. Stationery Office.

Tansley, A. G. (1944), *Journal of Ecology*, Volume 32.

Tansley, A. G. (1949), 2nd Edition, *The British Islands and their Vegetation*. Cambridge University Press, 2 vols.

The Nature Conservancy (1949-56), Annual Reports. H.M. Stationery Office, 5 vols.

Society for the Promotion of Nature Reserves (1925-56), Handbooks.

National Trust for Places of Historic Interest and Natural Beauty. Lists of Properties and Annual Reports.

National Parks Commission (1950-56), Annual Reports. H.M. Stationery Office, 6 vols.

Royal Society for the Protection of Birds (1891-1956), Annual Reports.

BEN LAWERS

National Trust for Scotland (1955), *Ben Lawers and its Alpine Flora*.

BLAKENEY POINT

Steers, J. A. (ed. 1952), *A Guide to Blakeney Point and Scolt Head Island*. London, National Trust.

CADER IDRIS

Evans, E. P. (1932), *Cader Idris: a Study of Certain Plant Communities in South-west Merionethshire*. J. Ecol., Vol. 20.

Evans, E. P. (1944), *Cader Idris and Craig-y-Benglog. The Study of the Distribution of floristically rich Localities in relation to Bedrock.* J. Ecol., Vol. 32.

CAIRNGORMS
Alexander, H. (1950), *The Cairngorms.* Edinburgh, Scottish Mountaineering Club.

Roger, J. Grant (1956), *Flowering Plants of the Cairngorms.* Cairngorm Club Journal.

CORS TREGARON
Godwin, H. and Conway, V. M. (1939), *The Ecology of a raised Bog near Tregaron, Cardiganshire.* J. Ecol., Vol. 27.

DUNGENESS
Steers, J. A. (1943), *The Coastline of England and Wales.* Cambridge, the University Press.

Steers, J. A. (1953), *The Sea Coast.* London, Collins.

FARNE ISLANDS
Watt, G. (1951), *The Farne Islands, their History and Wild Life.* London, Country Life, Ltd.

GIBRALTAR POINT
Lincolnshire Naturalists' Trust (1949-1955), Annual Reports of Bird Observatory and Field Research Station.

GRASSHOLM, PEMBS.
Gillham, Dr. Mary E. (1953), *An Ecological Account of the vegetation of Skokholm and Grassholm.* J. Ecol. Vol. 41.

HICKLING BROAD
Turner, E. L. (1924), *Broadland Birds.* London, Country Life, Ltd.

MINSMERE
Royal Society for the Protection of Birds (1952), *Minsmere Bird Reserve.*

MOOR HOUSE
Conway, V. M. (1955), *The Moor House National Nature Reserve, Westmorland.* S.P.N.R. Handbook, 1955.

NEWBOROUGH WARREN
North, F. J., Campbell, B. and Scott, R. (1949), *Snowdonia, the National Park of North Wales.* London, Collins.

NORTH RONA
 Darling, F. F. (1939), *A Naturalist on Rona: Essays of a Biologist in Isolation.* Oxford, Clarendon Press.

NOSS AND HERMANESS
 Fisher, J., Stewart, M. and Venables, L. S. V. (1939), *Gannet Colonies of Shetland.* British Birds, Vol. 32.

 Venables, L. S. V. and Venables, U. M. (1955), *Birds and Mammals of Shetland.* Edinburgh, Oliver & Boyd.

ORFORDNESS-HAVERGATE
 Royal Society for the Protection of Birds (1952), *Havergate Bird Reserve.*

SCOLT HEAD ISLAND
 Turner, E. L. (1928), *Bird Watching on Scolt Head.* London, Country Life Ltd.

 Steers, J. A. (ed. 1934), *Scolt Head Island—the Story of its Origin; the Plant and Animal Life of the Dunes and Marshes.* Norfolk and Norwich Nat. Soc.

 Steers, J. A. (ed. 1952), *A Guide to Blakeney Point and Scolt Head Island.* London, National Trust.

SKOKHOLM AND GRASSHOLM
 Lockley, R. M. (1938), *I Know an Island.* London, Harrap.

WICKEN FEN
 Gardiner, J. S. (ed. 1923-32), *The Natural History of Wicken Fen.* Cambridge, Bowes & Bowes. 6 vols.

 National Trust (1947), *A Guide to Wicken Fen.*

WYCHWOOD
 Watney, V. J. (1910), *Cornbury and the Forest of Wychwood.* London, priv. pr.

A full list of the number of sources consulted would require far more space than is available, but the Librarian of the Nature Conservancy, 19 Belgrave Square, London, S.W.1, will be glad to advise on relevant publications if so requested.

P

ADDRESSES OF RESERVE MANAGEMENTS

*The Reserves managed from each address are indicated
by numbers corresponding to those on map on page 6*

The Nature Conservancy,   2-4, 6-13, 15-16, 18-20,
    19, Belgrave Square, London, S.W.1.   21, 23, 27, 31-32, 39,
    Belgravia 3241.   41-44, 46, 60, 66-68, 70

The Nature Conservancy (Scotland),   72, 74-76, 78-87
    12, Hope Terrace, Edinburgh, 9.
    Edinburgh 57017.

The Nature Conservancy (Wales),   50-54
    School of Agriculture,
    University College of North Wales,
    Memorial Buildings, Bangor, Caerns.
    Bangor 412.

The National Trust for Places of Historic   40, 47, 65
Interest and Natural Beauty,
    42, Queen Anne's Gate, London, S.W.1.
    Whitehall 0211.

The National Trust for Scotland,   77
    5, Charlotte Square, Edinburgh, 2.
    Edinburgh 34872-3.

The Norfolk Naturalists Trust,   30, 33-38
    The Assembly House,
    Theatre Street, Norwich, Norfolk.

Yorkshire Naturalists' Trust, Ltd,   63
    Catton Hall, Thirsk, Yorkshire.
    Topcliffe 224.

Lincolnshire Naturalists' Trust,   55-58
    A. E. Smith, M.A. (Hon. Sec.),
    Pyewipes, Willoughby, Alford, Lincs.
    Willoughby 259.

Annet,   1
    Lt.-Cmdr. T. M. Dorrien-Smith,

Tresco Abbey,
Isles of Scilly, Cornwall.

The Clerk to the County Council,   71
Cumberland County Council,
The County Offices, Carlisle.
Carlisle 23456.

The Clerk to the County Council,   64
Durham County Council,
Shire Hall, Durham.
Durham 980-993.

The Clerk to the County Council,   73
East Lothian County Council,
County Buildings,
Haddington, East Lothian.
Haddington 3245.

Field Studies Council,   48
119, Finsbury Pavement, London, E.C.2.
Monarch 3852.

Forestry Commission,   24
1, Princes Gate, London, S.W.7.
Kensington 9691.

Humber Wildfowl Refuge Committee,   59
Frank Mason (Hon. Sec.),
8, Welburn Grove,
Bricknell Avenue, Hull, East Yorks.
Hull 19293.

The Clerk to the County Council,   62
North Riding of Yorkshire County Council,
County Hall, Northallerton, Yorks.
Northallerton 168-175.

University Chest Office,   22
Broad Street, Oxford.
Oxford 48491.

The Secretary,
Royal Society for the Protection of Birds,   14, 25, 26, 28, 49, 52
25, Eccleston Square, London, S.W.1.
Victoria 2412.

Society for the Promotion of Nature Reserves,   29, 61, 69
British Museum (Natural History),

Cromwell Road, London, S.W.7.
Kensington 6323.
The Town Clerk,   17
    Southend-on-Sea Borough Council,
    Municipal Buildings,
    Clarence Road, Southend-on-Sea, Essex.
    Southend 49451.
Steep Holm Trust,   5
    J. H. Savory (Hon. Sec.),
    61, Lower Redland Road, Bristol, 6.
West Wales Field Society,   48, 49
    D. G. Sansbury (Secretary),
    Is-y-Coed, Talybont, Cardiganshire.
Wildfowl Trust, The,   45
    Slimbridge, Gloucestershire.
    Cambridge (Glos.) 333.

INDEX

Figures in heavy type refer to pages on which illustrations appear.
Figures in brackets refer to pages where a plant is referred to under
an English but not under a Latin name or vice versa.